Contents

Part 1 The enquiry process

Part 2 Fieldwork in physical environments

Part 3 Fieldwork in human environments

Part 4 Preparing for Paper 3

AQA GCSE Geography Fieldwork Imprint and Acknowledgements

Insight and Perspective Ltd, 701 Stonehouse Park, Sperry Way, Stonehouse, Glos, GL10 3UT

www.insightandperspective.co.uk

Insight and Perspective Ltd 2018

First published 2018

10 9 8 7 6 5 4 3 2 1

ISBN 13: 978-1-912190-03-4

Designed and typeset by Wooden Ark
Printed by TJ International, Padstow, Cornwall, UK

Acknowledgements
The author and publishers would like to thank Sam Rudd, Christine Wise and Andy Leeder for their contributions when developing the Fieldwork in Action series.
The author and publishers would like to thank the following for permission to use the photographs/copyright material:
Front cover and p84 Field Studies Council; p16 OS Mapping of Shrewsbury © Crown copyright 2018 OS 93636185: p39 and pp100-101 parallel.co.uk; p39 www.police.uk; p61 hydrograph www.riverlevels.uk/esk; p109 Gemma Love.
All other photographs Andy Owen.

The publishers have made every effort to trace the copyright holders. If they have inadvertently overlooked any they will be pleased to acknowledge these at the first available opportunity.

Why do geographers do fieldwork?

Fieldwork is a really important part of geography. Designing a fieldwork investigation encourages you to be inquisitive and pose questions. Each fieldtrip teaches you useful skills about data collection and data analysis. After a fieldtrip you learn about different styles of maps and graphs – and why some are more suitable than others. Fieldwork also helps you understand the importance of evidence in constructing a persuasive piece of writing. Perhaps the most important skill that you will learn is how to evaluate your fieldwork. What were the strengths and limitations of your data collection or the ways you presented the data?

As a GCSE student you must do **two** fieldwork enquiries.
- One will investigate an aspect of physical geography such as rivers or coasts.
- The other will investigate an aspect of human geography such as urban or economic geography.

How to use this book

This book is designed to support you throughout your fieldwork enquiries and in preparing for your Paper 3 examination which assesses fieldwork skills and enquiries. There are four parts to the book:
- Part 01 The enquiry process;
- Part 02 Fieldwork in physical environments;
- Part 03 Fieldwork in human environments;
- Part 04 Preparing for Paper 3.

Part 01 The enquiry process

Check the learning objectives – they summarise what you will learn on this page.

Part 01 has 6 chapters – one for each stage of the enquiry process. Use these chapters as you plan your fieldwork and also when you get back from the fieldtrip to help you process the data, draw your graphs, and reach your conclusions.

Each part of the book has a different colour so you can find your way around easily.

Key fieldwork terms are in a bold coloured font – you can look them up in the glossary.

How to use this book

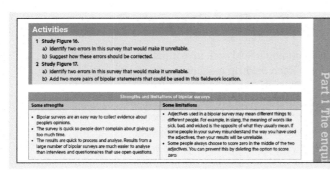

Activities – so you can check you have understood what you have learned.

Strengths and limitations help you evaluate fieldwork techniques. Learning how to evaluate your fieldwork is a really important skill – testing whether or not you can evaluate your fieldwork is one of the main points of the exam.

Part 02 Fieldwork in physical environments

Part 02 is about fieldwork investigations in a physical environment.

These bullet points give ideas about collecting data in your own fieldwork. They will also help you prepare for the exam and answer questions about fieldwork in an unfamiliar environment. This is because your fieldwork may have been in a coastal location but you may still be expected to answer questions about fieldwork on a river.

Photos help you to imagine how fieldwork could be collected.

Part 03 Fieldwork in Human environments

Part 03 is about fieldwork investigations in a human environment.

Step-by-step guides help you collect data.

Maps or graphs help you practise analysing patterns or evaluating techniques.

Practice questions will help you to prepare for the fieldwork questions in the Paper 3 exam.

Exam advice – tips to help you answer questions and understand command words.

Part 04 Preparing for Paper 3

Part 04 describes how you will be assessed in Paper 3. The exam paper has two sections and this part of the book will help you prepare for each of these sections.

Chapter 13 will help you prepare for Section A. In this section of the exam you need to refer to evidence in the Resources Booklet. This chapter will help you analyse the Resources Booklet in the weeks before the exam with lots of helpful tips and strategies.

Chapters 14 and 15 will help you prepare for Section B of Paper 3 – which is the part of the exam that assesses fieldwork. Chapter 14 gives tips about revising for this section of the exam. Chapter 15 gives advice about answering questions in the exam.

Practice questions about your own fieldwork

Student answers – comments from the examiner show how they would be marked.

Chapter 1

Creating an aim for fieldwork

Learning objectives
- Understanding the six stages of the enquiry process.
- How to identify an overall aim for your fieldwork.

Figure 1 The six stages of the fieldwork enquiry process.

Starting the enquiry process

At the heart of good fieldwork is the process of enquiry. In this process we ask questions and collect evidence to help answer those questions. A good fieldwork enquiry goes through six stages – these are shown in Figure 1. Understanding each of these stages is important if you want to do well in your fieldwork.

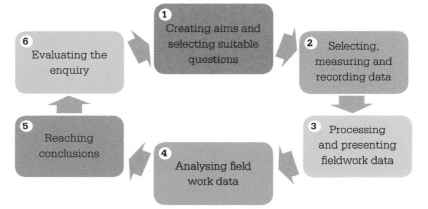

1. Creating aims and selecting suitable questions
2. Selecting, measuring and recording data
3. Processing and presenting fieldwork data
4. Analysing field work data
5. Reaching conclusions
6. Evaluating the enquiry

Choosing an aim

You can't just start your fieldwork by going outside and measuring things or counting stuff. Fieldwork involves a lot of counting and measuring but this data collection has to have a purpose so you will need an aim. There are three main ways to give your fieldwork enquiry an aim.

1. **Investigate a geographical** process to see how it works in the real world. For example, you could investigate the process of longshore drift on a beach, or the deposition of pebbles in a river. You could investigate the process of regeneration in a town or city.
2. **Survey people's opinions about a geographical issue**. This may be some controversial change that is affecting your local area such as the building of a new housing estate on a greenfield site.
3. **Investigate a geographical concept**. Concepts are the big ideas that help us make sense of the world around us. Concepts help us break down complex patterns and make connections. Figure 2 lists some useful concepts.

You also need to know where your fieldwork is going to take place. Will you be working in a river environment, a beach, or in a town? A little local knowledge may help you to identify an interesting issue that could be investigated. Thinking about the location and a process, issue, or concept, will help you create an aim for your fieldwork.

Concept	What is this concept about?
Cause and effect	Geographical features and processes have positive and negative effects on the environment surrounding them.
Cycles and flows	Environments contain flows, for example, flows of water through a drainage basin, or flows of people through a city. We can investigate factors that influence the size and rate of these flows.
Inequality	Services such as sports facilities or social care are rarely distributed evenly. We can investigate whether one place, or one group of people, has more than its fair share of something.
Mitigating risk	All environments contain risks such as river or coastal floods. We can investigate how these risks can be reduced (or mitigated) or managed.
Place	Each place has features that give that place a unique character. This character gives the people who live in that place a sense of identity.
Sustainability	Sustainability is a measure of how well a place or environment is coping with social, economic, or environmental change.

Figure 2 Geographical concepts that can be investigated through fieldwork.

For example in Figure 3, we could investigate:

- a process like gentrification;
- an issue such as traffic congestion and pollution;
- the concept of risk.

Only after you have created an aim for the fieldwork can you give your investigation a title. A title could be a simple statement that reflects the aim of your investigation:

An investigation of the issue of traffic congestion in Cowbridge Road.

Alternatively, you could choose a title that that reflects the main question that you want to answer, such as:

How can Cowbridge Road be made safer for pedestrians and cyclists?

Figure 3 Which aim would you investigate here? Cowbridge Road East, Cardiff.

Aim 1 to investigate how traffic flows vary through the day.

Aim 2 to investigate whether house prices are affected by traffic noise.

Aim 3 to investigate how this environment can be made safer for pedestrians and local residents.

Aim 4 to investigate how local people feel about their community. What features do they like, dislike, and identiy with?

Activities

1 **Study Figure 3. If you were able to visit this location on a fieldtrip:**
   a) how might counting the traffic help you answer one or more of these aims?
   b) what other data could you collect to help you answer each of these aims?
2 **Each of the aims in Figure 3 is connected to one of the concepts listed in Figure 2.**
   a) Match the aims to the concepts.
   b) Suggest one other concept that could be investigated here. Explain your choice.

What makes a good enquiry question?

You can use questions to break down your aim into manageable chunks but what makes a good enquiry question? To help you ask your own enquiry questions you could use the question starters that have been added to Figure 4.

Figure 4 Dovedale in the Peak District National Park. Dovedale is a honeypot site that attracts thousands of visitors, especially at weekends.

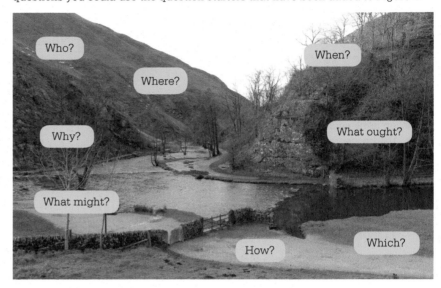

Figure 5 gives three different styles of question.

- Questions on the left are useful but not very demanding because the answers are probably very straightforward.
- The questions in the middle are better. They are more useful and interesting as enquiry questions because they are about the relationship between two variables.
- The questions on the right are more interesting again and could provide excellent enquiry questions because you may find a variety of potential answers. However, this type of question needs to be phrased very carefully and you may need to gather a great deal of evidence to answer them fully.

Figure 5 Styles of enquiry question.

	increasing complexity of question ⟶		
	Questions that have a straightforward answer	Questions about connections	Questions that have a complex answer
Examples of question starter	When? Where? How many? Which?	How does? What effect would?	Who benefits? What ought? Who should?
Examples of questions	Which is the busiest shopping street? When is the busiest time of day? How many cars pass in 5 minutes?	How does wind speed vary with altitude? What effect would traffic noise have on house prices?	Who would benefit most if flood protection was improved? What ought to be done to make this community more sustainable?

Choosing a hypothesis

Just like a science experiment, you can sometimes use geography fieldwork to prove, or disprove, a hypothesis. A **hypothesis** is a provisional idea which can be proven to be correct, or incorrect, based on the factual evidence collected in your fieldwork. An example of a hypothesis that could be investigated in Figure 4 is:

Footpath erosion is greater closest to the car park.

Once you have chosen a suitable hypothesis for your fieldwork you should state the **null hypothesis**. This is what you would discover if the hypothesis was incorrect. For Figure 3, the null hypothesis would be:

There is no difference in the amount of footpath erosion with increasing distance from the car park.

Setting a SMART aim

Is your aim a good one? Is it suitable? An aim shouldn't be too simple. For example, *'How many cars travel down this road in 5 minutes?'* is not an aim. This simple question is part of the broader aim of investigating patterns of commuter movement. However, an aim shouldn't be too complex either – otherwise you may not be able to achieve it. For example, *'Cowbridge Road East is a perfect example of a modern sustainable residential community'* would be very difficult to prove, or disprove, because the word 'perfect' is so difficult to measure. Your aim should be SMART – see Figure 6.

Is your aim SMART?
- **Specific** – does the aim have a clear focus?
- **Measurable** – can you collect and count data?
- **Achievable** – will it be safe? Will you need a team of people? Is data available?
- **Realistic** – have you got the right skills and/or equipment?
- **Timely** – will you have enough time during the fieldtrip to collect all of the data?

Figure 6 Making your aim SMART

Take a virtual visit

Another good way to prepare for your fieldwork is to make a virtual visit. Use the internet to see the environment you will be working in before the day of the fieldtrip. This has a number of advantages. It will help you to:
- pose enquiry questions or set a hypothesis that relates to the actual place that you will visit;
- plan where you could collect the data;
- consider potential risks of the site and plan your visit so you stay safe.

Activities

1 **Study Figure 4.**
   a) Write 10 enquiry questions using as many different question starters as you can.
   b) Evaluate your questions using Figure 5. Which are your best three questions? Are they SMART? Are they complex?

Learning objectives

- How to identify potential risks.
- Steps you can take to reduce these risks.

Figure 7 Busy roads can be a risk. Only cross where it is safe.

Figure 8 Potential risks and how to reduce them.

Risk assessment

You need to stay safe during your fieldwork, so it is important to think about any potential risks that you and your classmates might face. If you can identify the potential risks, then you can think about specific ways that the danger can be reduced or removed completely. For example, if you are working next to a busy road you must stay on the pavement. If you have to cross the road, then only do so at a safe location – preferably at a crossing point that is controlled by lights as in Figure 7. Figure 8 lists some potential risks you could face during fieldwork and ways these risks can be reduced.

Potential risk	How this risk can be reduced
Being trapped on a beach by the rising tide. Risk of drowning.	Check the tide table before the visit. Do not work on the beach as the tide is rising.
Strong winds blow sand from the beach. Risk of eye injury.	Check the weather forecast before the visit. Do not work in sand dunes when there are strong onshore winds.
Rocks falling from cliffs above.	Do not work at the top of a beach immediately below a cliff.
Falling on a steep slope and suffering a serious injury to limbs or head.	Do not work close to the top of a cliff. Keep to paths on slopes.
Slipping on wet grass and twisting an ankle.	Wear walking boots rather than trainers.
Falling into a river and suffering an injury or hypothermia. Risk of drowning.	Do not run next to the river. Wear walking boots. Students working in a river must not go in above knees and always work in teams. Check the weather forecast before the visit.
Being hit by a car/cyclist when crossing the road.	Only cross roads where visibility in both directions is good or where there is a pelican or zebra crossing.
Trip hazards when walking through undergrowth.	Wear walking boots. Move slowly and carefully.
Low branches in a woodland. Risk of eye injury.	Keep to paths. Do not run.
Tunnelling in sand dunes. Risk of collapse and suffocation.	Do not play in sand dunes and never dig or tunnel.

Think of others

As well as identifying potential risks, there are some things we can all do during a fieldtrip to keep safe. These tips should make your experience of fieldwork pleasant as well as safe.

- Listen to your teacher's instructions carefully.
- Work in pairs or small teams. Look after each other.
- Wear sensible clothing and shoes so you stay warm and safe.
- Be aware of hazards around you. Look out for warning signs, like Figure 9, if you are working in an environment that is potentially dangerous.

Figure 9 A sign warning of risk at the coast, West Wales.

Figure 10 A beach at Happisburgh, Norfolk.

Activities

1 Study Figure 10.

a) Identify three potential risks of doing fieldwork in this location.

b) Suggest how each risk could be reduced.

Chapter 2
How is evidence collected?

Types of data

In a fieldwork enquiry we need to collect data that will provide the evidence we need to answer our aims. We describe data as either **quantitative** or **qualitative**.

Quantitative data is something you can count, or measure. Some evidence that you can measure will need specialist equipment. For example you measure:

- wind speed with an anemometer;
- river velocity with a flow meter;
- slope angles with a clinometer.

However, lots of quantitative data can be simply counted such as the number of vehicles on a road, the number (and type) of shops, and the number of pedestrians in a shopping centre.

Qualitative data is something that helps us to describe a place or geographical issue with words or pictures rather than by measuring with numbers. It can include interviews, making field sketches, or taking photographs, videos, or audio recordings.

Figure 1 Examples of quantitative and qualitative data

Quantitative data	Qualitative data
Depth and width of a river Wind speed House prices The size of pebbles on a beach	Whether pedestrians feel safe in the city centre Whether people prefer shopping in the high street or out of town What different groups of people think about the risk of flooding

Activities

1 **Make a copy of Figure 1. Decide whether each statement below is quantitative or qualitative and then add it to the correct column.**

The number of wave crests that break each minute on a beach.

Photos of features of an urban environment that provide evidence of sustainability.

The reasons people move to live somewhere new.

A field sketch of a coastal landform.

The angle of slope of a beach.

Photos of features of a shopping centre that are liked/disliked by shoppers.

Noise (in decibels) of traffic from a road.

An audio recording of a busy shopping street.

Infiltration rates of water soaking into different soils.

Wind speeds at different locations up a hill.

What is the difference between discrete and continuous data?

Discrete data and continuous data are two different types of quantitative data. **Discrete data** can be counted. We could count how many people are in a shopping street, or how many vehicles pass along a street. That would be discrete data. By contrast, **continuous data** is measured. We can measure how quickly the river is flowing, or how much noise the traffic is making. That would be continuous data. Distance, velocity and time are all examples of continuous data that are often measured in geography fieldwork.

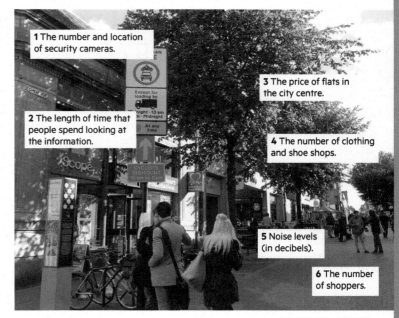

1 The number and location of security cameras.

2 The length of time that people spend looking at the information.

3 The price of flats in the city centre.

4 The number of clothing and shoe shops.

5 Noise levels (in decibels).

6 The number of shoppers.

Figure 2 Examples of discrete and continuous data that could be collected in a retail environment, Lancaster

What is the difference between primary and secondary data?

The data you collect during the fieldtrip, such as the number of vehicles passing, or the answers to a questionnaire, is known as **primary data**. Sometimes you will be able to answer your aim by only collecting primary data. However, a lot of data has already been collected and is available in books and on websites. This is **secondary data**. There are lots of forms of secondary data that might be useful to help you answer your fieldwork enquiry. With careful research, you can find:

- photographs that show your fieldwork location, both now and in the past - you could annotate these to show how the location has changed;
- blogs – you can analyse people's viewpoints;
- maps - for example, the Environment Agency Flood Map would be useful if your fieldwork is located in a town that is at risk of river or coastal flooding;
- tables of data – which you can use to draw your own graphs.

Strengths and limitations of primary and secondary data		
	Strengths	**Some limitations**
Primary data	You know exactly how the data was collected.	Your sampling strategy may not be representative (see pages 14-15).
Secondary data	It's much quicker to download secondary data than collect your own primary data.	You may not know how or when it was collected and the figures may be out of date.

Activities

2 **Study Figure 2.**
   a) Sort the quantitative data into discrete and continuous types.
   b) Suggest three examples of qualitative data that could be collected here.

Why do I need a sampling strategy?

Imagine you want to see how the amount of traffic varies throughout the day in a small commuter town. It wouldn't be possible to count every single vehicle travelling along every road for 24 hours. It would take too much time. Also, you would need your friends to agree to help you because you can't watch every road at the same time. So, instead of trying to collect every bit of data, you will need to collect a **sample** of data. If collected properly, your sample will accurately represent the patterns or trends shown in all of the data.

What sampling strategies are available?

Figure 3 Four commonly used sampling strategies

There are various ways you can select your sample. Figure 3 summarises four main strategies that you could use.

Sampling strategy	How it works	Examples – you collect data...
Systematic	Your sample is chosen at regular intervals. Every n^{th} item is sampled.	• at points that are equally spaced (for example, every 10 metres) along a line (transect) • every hour • by interviewing the 10th, 20th and 30th person who passes you
Random	Your data is sampled at random intervals. Every item has an equal chance of being sampled.	• at places that have been chosen by using tables of random numbers to generate grid references • in streets chosen by putting all street names into a bag and pulling out a sample of names at random
Stratified	Your data falls into two or more categories. You make sure that your sample reflects the proportions that fall in each category.	• by sampling plants and wind speeds in a sand dune. You choose 50% of your sampling points on slopes that face the sea and 50% of your sample points on slopes that face away from the sea • you are sampling how students at your school feel about a geographical issue. 45% of the students are in Years 7 to 9, 40% are in Years 10 and 11, 15% are in the sixth form. You make sure that your questionnaire is given out in these proportions
Opportunistic (also known as convenience sampling)	Your data is scarce so you take the opportunity to collect data whenever or wherever you can.	• by asking a questionnaire of every tourist you can find • you intended to systematically sample downstream along the course of a river. However, a lot of the sites you wanted to sample were on private land so you sampled wherever there was a public footpath next to the river.

Sampling along a line

Figure 4 By collecting data at regular intervals across this river channel the students are sampling systematically along a line.

In many fieldwork enquiries a hypothesis will try to investigate how something changes over distance. For example:

rivers get wider as you go downstream;

noise reduces as you get further away from a busy road;

house prices get higher as you get closer to the park.

Each of these hypotheses could be investigated by sampling data along a line. You can use any of the four main sampling strategies while you work along a line. Sampling along a line is often described as a **transect**.

Sampling across an area

People say that if you can map it, it's geography! This is because geographers are interested in how features are distributed. The patterns we see on a map are known as **spatial** patterns. If you sample along a line you are sampling in one dimension. You will see how a pattern changes with distance but you will not be able to see a spatial pattern. To see a spatial pattern (and then draw a map) you will need to sample in two dimensions. You could do this by:

- sampling along several lines, for example, four lines radiating out from the town centre towards the suburbs;
- using a map of a town to identify sampling locations at each grid intersection. This would be a form of systematic sampling.

Which is the best sampling strategy for me?

Each sampling method has advantages and disadvantages which makes it more suitable in some situations than others.

- Random sampling provides an unbiased sample. If the full size of the thing that is being sampled is quite small (like shops in a town, or students in a year group) this method should create a sample that represents the whole accurately – we say that it is **representative** of the whole.
- Systematic sampling is much quicker and simpler than random sampling. It's a better method to use if the thing that is being sampled is quite large (like a questionnaire of shoppers, or plants along a line through an ecosystem). Systematic sampling across an area should generate enough data to draw a map.
- When the thing that is being sampled is very large (for example, pebbles on a beach), you can combine random and systematic sampling strategies (see pages 18-19).
- Opportunistic sampling is really a method that you choose because it is not practical to choose another method. It may be quicker or easier than other methods but the results may not be representative.

http://www.textfixer.com/numbers/random-number-generator.php One of many online tools that will generate random numbers for you.

Ordnance Survey (OS) maps

Learning objectives
- How to use an OS map to design a sampling strategy.
- How to give 4 and 6 figure references.

You can use an **Ordnance Survey (OS) map** to design your sampling strategy before the fieldtrip. Figure 5 is an extract from a 1:50,000 map which means that 1cm on the map is equal to 50,000cm (500m) on the ground. A 1:50,000 scale map is useful for planning fieldwork in a town. For coastal or rivers fieldwork a 1:25,000 map is more useful because it shows more detail.

Figure 5 1:50,000 OS map extract of Shrewsbury.

Using an OS map to sample along a line

You can use an OS map to plan the route of a transect (or cross section). For example, in Figure 5, we could sample traffic, noise, and house prices at regular intervals along the A458 to investigate how and why house prices vary with distance from the town centre. First, use the map to calculate the total length of the transect. It is about 4,500 metres from the edge of the town in grid square 4513 to the town centre, so we could sample at regular intervals of 500 metres to create a sample of 10 sites with one sample point at each end of the transect.

Sampling across an area

The light blue grid lines on an OS map divide your fieldwork area into a grid. You can use this to design a systematic sampling strategy that will give two dimensional (2D) data that can be represented on a map later. For example, we could use Figure 5 to design a systematic sampling strategy for Shrewsbury using the following steps.

Step One Design an EQI (Environmental Quality Index) survey (see pages 28-29) that can be used to investigate how quality of life or access to services varies across the town.

Step Two Identify each grid square that contains part of Shrewsbury. There are 24 out of 28 grid squares in Figure 5. You could work in teams and allocate 4 squares to each team.

Step Three Carry out one EQI survey within each grid square.

Checking access

OS maps are also useful for checking that you will have access to places that you would like to survey. In a river survey, for example, students often plan to sample at regular intervals along the stream. However, in reality, some sample points cannot be accessed because they are on private land. This means that survey points are chosen by opportunistic sampling because students actually sample the river where they have access. In Figure 5 you can see that the stream in grid square 5011 has a public footpath next to it so access would be possible.

Grid references

Grid references are useful to identify sample sites, for example, the location of an EQI survey, a field sketch, or a photograph. You can give two types of grid reference.

- A four figure grid reference identifies a complete grid square.
- A six figure grid reference pinpoints a single place within one grid square.

Step Four Measure tenths between the grid lines (2mm on the 1:50,000 scale map). This gives the third and sixth digit of a 6 figure reference.
The rail station is at 495129

Step Two Read up the northings

Step Three The intersection of these grid lines gives a 4 figure grid reference for the orange grid square.
This square is at 4912

Step One Read along the eastings

Figure 6 How to give four and six figure grid references.

Activities

1 **Design a transect with 10 regularly spaced sampled points that starts at Lower Edgebold (in the bottom left of the map) and ends at the train station.**
   a) Give a six figure reference for the start of the transect.
   b) How long is the transect?
   c) How far apart are the sample points?
   d) How many sample points are in the countryside before the edge of the town?

Learning objectives
■ How to sample data
using a quadrat.

Sampling data using a quadrat

A quadrat is a simple square frame that you place on the ground. It gives you a shape that you can sample inside. The frame is usually quite small – often 50cm by 50cm (which is a quarter of a square metre) - like the one shown in Figure 7. However, you can also use tent pegs and string to mark out a larger frame – say 2 metres by 2 metres. The frame is often divided into smaller squares with wire or string to make it easier to identify sample locations within the square.

Quadrats are used to help sample a very large population by breaking down a large space into smaller, more manageable spaces – concentrating on the space within the frame of each quadrat. They are often used to sample plants (for example, in a sand dune ecosystem) or pebbles (on a beach).

There are two main ways to use a quadrat.

■ **One** Sample objects within the quadrat using the points where the internal wires/strings cross – in other words, at the intersections. Use them systematically, for example, by sampling pebbles at every intersection, as in Figure 7.

■ **Two** When you are sampling types of vegetation, it is usual to estimate the area covered by each type of plant within the quadrat, as in Figure 8. Do this by counting the squares (the spaces between the wires/strings). The quadrat in Figure 8 is divided into 100 squares so it is easy to estimate the percentage distribution of each plant as each square represents 1%. This style of quadrat works best with low growing plants. The quadrat in Figure 7 has five rows and five columns of spaces between the strings. That makes 25 small squares inside the quadrat. The quadrat represents 100% of the sample area, so each small square represents 4% of the whole (because 100 divided by 25=4). This style of quadrat could be used to estimate percentage area covered by taller plants.

Quadrats are often used to sample vegetation along a belt transect. For more information on this technique, you can use page 87.

Figure 7 A quadrat being used to sample pebbles on a beach. The stone under each intersection was measured.

Control groups

Quadrats are often used to measure how vegetation changes in relation to another variable, for example, how vegetation varies:

- across a sand dune with increasing distance from the sea;
- across a footpath with variable amounts of trampling.

When you are looking for variations like this it is a good idea to see what the vegetation is like by sampling in an area unaffected by the variable. We call this a **control group**. It allows you to compare the results of the area that you are investigating (for example, the plants that have been trampled on the footpath) with the normal vegetation of the area.

Figure 8 Estimating areas within the frame of the quadrat. The percentage of the quadrat occupied by each species of plant was estimated. Three different species of plant can be identified in this quadrat. The second image has been tinted to show the percentage area covered by each plant more clearly.

Dos and don'ts of using quadrats

Do:	Don't:
✓ Select locations for the quadrat using a systematic, random, or stratified technique. ✓ Take care to avoid damaging the vegetation where you are working.	✗ Throw the quadrat over your shoulder. This doesn't make the sampling random and it could be dangerous! ✗ Select pebbles from within the quadrat at random by just picking some out. Your eye will be drawn to the larger, or more interesting, looking pebbles. This means your sample won't be representative.

Strengths and limitations of using quadrats	
Some strengths	Some limitations
Quadrats are useful for sampling a very large population (like pebbles or plants) that is spread over a large area. You can use quadrats to record the presence or absence of a variable (whether it is in the quadrat or not) and also the frequency of a variable (how much of the variable is present). Quadrats are relatively cheap pieces of equipment and simple to use.	It can be difficult to be accurate about the percentage of vegetation in a quadrat if the plants are different heights. Taller plants grow over shorter ones so it is possible to underestimate the percentage of the quadrat filled by smaller plants.

Using fieldwork equipment

A lot of data can be collected without the need for any special equipment. You will not need special equipment to collect qualitative data through **bipolar surveys**, **Likert surveys**, and **questionnaires**, although you will need to design a data collection sheet before the fieldwork begins (see pages 22-23).

Quantitative data that is continuous will need to be measured and some will need specialist fieldwork equipment. Wind speed, for example, needs to be measured using an anemometer, like the one in Figure 9. However, other measurements are easier to make. For example, in the river fieldwork seen in Figure 4 on page 14:

- the width of the river is measured using a measuring tape;
- the depth of water is measured using a metre rule;
- the velocity of river flow can be calculated by floating a dog biscuit downstream for 10 metres and using the stop watch app on your smart phone.

Figure 9 An anemometer is used to measure wind speed

Using a clinometer

A clinometer is used to measure angles from the horizontal so, in fieldwork, it can be used to measure the angle of a slope. A traditional clinometer includes a swinging arm or weight. As the clinometer is tipped up to the same angle as the slope, the weight points vertically downwards so that you can measure the angle. Alternatively, you could download a free clinometer app onto your smartphone, like the one shown in Figure 10.

To measure the slope of a beach, like the one in Figure 10, you will need:

- a clinometer (or an app on your smartphone);
- two people;
- a long measuring tape;
- two ranging poles (although these are not essential);
- a data recording sheet.

Step One Set up a transect, up and down the beach, using the long measuring tape.

Step Two Identify the **breaks in slope** along the transect. These are places where the gradient of the slope suddenly changes. The photograph in Figure 10 has been coloured so that you can see the breaks in slope.

Step Three Start measuring at the bottom of the slope. If you do not have ranging poles, work with someone who is the same height as you. Get your partner to stand at the next break in slope. Hold the clinometer up to your eye and look along it into your partner's eyes. The angle recorded by the clinometer is the angle of the slope.

Step Four Record the angle (in degrees) and the distance between the start of the transect and the first break in slope (in metres) on your data recording sheet.

Step Five Later you can present your data as a line graph using a ruler and protractor. This graph will represent the shape of the **beach profile.**

Step Six Move up the transect to the first break in slope. Your partner should also move up the transect and stand at the next break in slope. Take the measurements and repeat this process until you have completed the transect.

Figure 10 Using a clinometer to measure slope angles on a beach. The dotted black line represents the transect. Notice that the red dashed line is parallel to the slope.

Dos and don'ts of using a clinometer

Do:

✔ Check that the tide is going out before you start. Then you can start the transect at the lowest part of the beach without any danger.

✔ Take three angle readings at each break in slope and take a mean. Clinometers that use a swinging arm can be affected by the wind. Calculating the mean will improve the reliability of your results.

Don't:

✘ Work with someone who is a different height unless you are using ranging poles. If you line up the clinometer with a colleague's eye and they are much taller than you are then your angle reading will be too large.

Site	Distance (metres) between sites	Angle (°) between sites
1 – 2	10	5
2 – 3	22	8
3 – 4	20	10
4 – 5	26	15
5 – 6	22	8
6 – 7	30	6
7 – 8	40	10
8 – 9	50	15
9 – 10	20	20
10 – 11	40	5
11 – 12	30	3

Figure 11 This data was collected by students measuring slope angles on a beach in the UK

Activities

1. Present the information from Figure 11 as a line graph to show the beach profile. You will need graph paper and a protractor to do this accurately. Plot distance from the sea on the horizontal axis. For sites 1-2 draw a straight line of 10 metres length from the origin (0) at an angle of 5°. From the end of this line draw a line of 22 metres length at an angle of 8°. Continue until all the data is plotted.
2. Annotate your line graph to show significant features of the beach profile, such as breaks in slope.

Designing data collection sheets

Now you know what data you want to collect there is one more important job to do before you go on your fieldtrip. You will need a quick and methodical way to record the evidence that you collect on your fieldtrip – so you need to design data collection sheets.

Your data collection sheet needs to be easy to use. Always record when and where the data was collected at the top of the sheet. Data can be broken down into categories (for example, size of pebbles, or age of people) and you can then add boxes or tables to your sheet so you can record results in each category. Using a tally mark, like Figure 12, is a good way to collect information that you are counting.

Continuous data, such as wind speed and noise levels, can vary considerably as you are measuring them. It's a good idea, therefore, to create several boxes for these values on your data collection sheet, like in Figure 14. Take 5 readings, one every 30 seconds. Then take an average.

Lots of students start a questionnaire, or bipolar survey, by recording the gender and age of the person they are talking to but this often isn't necessary. You should only do this if age or gender are factors that you want to analyse as part of your enquiry. For example, it would be essential to record the age of the respondents in your questionnaire if your enquiry question was 'Are older people more aware of risk in the environment than younger people?'.

Traffic survey

Location ..HIGH STREET.........
Date .19/05.. Time .11.4m...

Type	Tally	Total
Cycles	////	4
Motorbikes	//	2
Cars	HHT HHT HHT ////	19
Vans	HHT HHT	10
Lorries	HHT /	6
Buses	HHT	5

Figure 12 Use tally marks when you are counting things.

Beach survey data collection sheet

Date ......

Site 1

Pebble sizes (mm)	Number of pebbles
Less than 10	
10-20	
25-40	
40-50	
More than 50	

Figure 13 There are three errors in this data collection sheet. Can you spot them?

Location of noise readings ....

Time they were taken ....

Readings (one taken every 30 seconds)	Noise level (dB)
1	
2	
3	
4	
5	
Total	
Average (total/5)	

Figure 14 Design your data collection sheet so that several readings can be taken because noise readings may vary a lot.

Pilot surveys

If you are going to use a questionnaire (see pages 26-27) you will want to use some closed and some open questions. **Open questions** allow the person you are interviewing to say whatever they want in response. The following are examples of open questions that you might use in a fieldwork enquiry about place and identity.

1. Which features do you like best about this town?
2. What makes this town different from others you know well?
3. What gives this place its unique identity?

Using open questions like these have advantages but it is time consuming to record all the possible responses that people might give. So, it's a good idea to use a **pilot survey** with a few people to see what kinds of answers you are likely to get when you carry out the full survey. After the pilot survey, you can look at the answers that people gave and put them into categories. So, in a pilot survey, the open question *'Which features do you like best about this town?'* was asked. Imagine that:

Figure 15 Using a pilot survey to create option boxes for the data collection sheet.

- 5 people said friendly people;
- 4 people talked about history or historic buildings;
- 3 people said that good schools were an important feature of the town;
- 3 people said they liked the multicultural atmosphere;
- 1 person talked about locally owned (independent) shops.

As a result of this pilot survey you can now design a data collection sheet for your full questionnaire that looks like Figure 15.

Activities

1 **Study Figure 13. Identify three errors in the design of this data collection sheet.**
2 **Explain why it would be important to use a pilot survey to create the data collection sheet in Figure 15 rather than just making up the categories.**

1. Which features do you like best about this town?
Tick up to 3 boxes.

The people ☐

The town's history ☐

Buildings/architecture ☐

Local schools ☐

Cultural activities ☐

Multicultural atmosphere ☐

Independent shops ☐

Others ☐

If others, please describe the feature(s) …

Learning objectives
■ Knowing how to construct a Bipolar Survey.
■ Understanding their strengths and limitations.

Qualitative surveys and interviews

In some geography fieldwork we want to investigate people's ideas, opinions, or perceptions. This is an example of **qualitative data** and we can collect this type of evidence through surveys, questionnaires, and interviews. We can use **bipolar Surveys** and **Likert Surveys** (pronounced lick it) to collect evidence about the strength of people's opinions. These surveys use **closed questions** – the people who take part have to choose the answer they think they most agree with.

A closed question is the type of question that needs a simple response: the person has to answer yes/no, or tick a box. Multiple choice tests use closed questions. This technique is good because it is quick and easy to analyse the results – you just count up the number of people who respond in each way.

Bipolar surveys

Bipolar Surveys use pairs of statements that are opposite to one another. The people who take part in the survey have to decide where their opinion fits on the scale between these opposing statements.

A basic bipolar survey uses pairs of adjectives. Figure 16 gives an example that could be used to assess how people feel about one place. We could use this type of survey to investigate how different people perceive the same place. It could be a town, village, honeypot site or coastal landscape. For example:
■ whether younger people are more positive about a place than older people
■ whether visitors see more positives in a place than local people.

We can also use bipolar surveys to investigate opinions about a variety of different places. For example, to investigate how quality of life varies across a town or city. You don't even have to ask other people to do the survey – you and your classmates could fill it in. You would need to decide on a sampling technique to choose the places – perhaps conducting the survey every 200 metres along a transect that starts in the town centre and ends in the suburbs. If so, your bipolar survey could be one strand of evidence to investigate a hypothesis such as:

Quality of life improves towards the suburbs

Figure 16 A simple bipolar survey uses pairs of opposite adjectives.

	+3	+2	+1	0	-1	-2	-3	
Attractive								Unattractive
Quiet								Noisy
Peaceful								Calm
Safe								Unsafe
Dirty								Clean
Friendly								Unfriendly

A slightly more sophisticated bipolar survey uses opposing descriptions instead of simple adjectives. An example is shown in Figure 17. If the descriptions are well written, it should be possible for different people to use this type of survey consistently – meaning that the results of your survey will be more reliable than the basic type.

http://www.thesaurus.com/
Use the search engine to find synonyms (similar words) and antonyms (opposite words).

Figure 17 This bipolar survey could be used to test people's perception of a residential area.

Positive	+2	+1	0	-1	-2	Negative
Housing well-maintained						Housing in poor condition
Not much traffic						Very difficult to cross the road
Wide pavements						No pavements
Streets are well lit at night						No street lighting
Area feels safe. There is no graffiti						Area feels unsafe. There is a lot of graffiti and litter

Figure 18 A residential area in Grangetown, Cardiff.

Dos and don'ts of bipolar surveys

Do:
- ✓ Make sure that the pairs of statements are actually opposites.
- ✓ Put the statements the right way around in the table – so that positive statements get a positive score.

Don't:
- ✗ Make your statements too complicated or try to assess two things at once in one pair of statements, for example, Quiet and attractive > > > > > Noisy and unattractive

Activities

1 **Study Figure 16.**
   a) Identify two errors in this survey that would make it unreliable.
   b) Suggest how these errors should be corrected.
2 **Study Figure 17.**
   a) Identify two errors in this survey that would make it unreliable.
   b) Add two more pairs of bipolar statements that could be used in this fieldwork location.

Strengths and limitations of bipolar surveys	
Some strengths	**Some limitations**
• Bipolar surveys are an easy way to collect evidence about people's opinions. • The survey is quick so people don't complain about giving up too much time. • The results are quick to process and analyse. Results from a large number of bipolar surveys are much easier to analyse than interviews and questionnaires that use open questions.	• Adjectives used in a bipolar survey may mean different things to different people. For example, in slang, the meaning of words like sick, bad, and wicked is the opposite of what they usually mean. If some people in your survey misunderstand the way you have used the adjectives, then your results will be unreliable. • Some people always choose to score zero in the middle of the two adjectives. You can prevent this by deleting the option to score zero.

Likert Surveys and Questionnaires

As well as bipolar surveys, we can use Likert Surveys, questionnaires, and longer interviews to gather evidence about people's opinions.

Questionnaires and interviews

Questionnaires and interviews allow people to talk openly and in detail about a geographical issue. In both of these types of survey the interviewer needs to prepare some questions so that the survey has a common structure each time it is used. This will allow you to compare the responses of different people and make the data more reliable. In your analysis you can then look for common patterns and similarities as well as differences between the responses.

A **questionnaire** uses a mixture of closed and **open questions**. The closed questions will allow you to collect a lot of data quite quickly. The open questions allow the interviewee to say what they want, without having to choose from a list of set responses. The advantage of using open questions is that people sometimes say things you didn't expect. This means that open questions may allow you to collect some new and surprising evidence. However, it can be time consuming to analyse the results of open questions so it's a good idea to only use a few open questions if you plan to survey a large number of people.

Interviews only use open questions so they can provide a wide variety of responses. It is a good idea to make an audio recording of each interview so you can listen to them again. That will help you to focus on the words people use and analyse any differences and similarities between what people say. See pages 62-63 to find out how to analyse text. To save time you may decide to interview only a small sample of people. The disadvantage of this is the views you record may not represent the views of everyone in the community.

Dos and don'ts of questionnaires

Do:
- Be polite and courteous.
- Carry out a pilot survey (see pages 22-23) to identify any potential problems with the way your questions are worded.
- Use a mixture of closed and open questions.

Don't:
- Ask two things in one question, for example, 'Do you think that the new hotel would be good for local businesses and the environment?'
- Ask people about their age or gender unless your aim is to see whether certain groups of people have a different point of view.

Activities

1 **Study Figure 19.**
   a) Use this poster to design an enquiry question or hypothesis.
   b) Identify one more statement that could be added to the Likert Survey in Figure 20.
   c) Draft three open questions you could use to investigate the proposed new hotel in St Davids.

Likert Surveys

In a Likert survey we ask people to what extent they agree, or disagree, with one or more statements. The statements could be about any geographical issue where different people might have strong points of view. We would use this type of survey to investigate whether some groups of people have a different point of view to another group. For example, we could use a Likert Survey to investigate whether people agree:

- with building houses on a greenfield site;
- that flood defences need improving/strengthening;
- that tourism is good for the local area;
- with the closure of a rural service such as the village post office.

It may be that younger people have a different point of view to older people, or that local residents tend to take one point of view while visitors take another. Different points of view, and the reasons for them, maybe the aim of your investigation. If so, you will need to design a data collection sheet that records this information. An example is shown in Figure 20. Then, when you analyse the results of your survey, sort the responses by type first (by age group, or by local/visitor) before tallying up the scores for agree/disagree.

Figure 19 A poster in the street in St Davids, Pembroke. In 2017 some local people were protesting about plans to build a Premier Inn Hotel in the town.

Figure 20 A Likert Survey that could be used to investigate opinions about the building of a new hotel.

Please tick the box that best describes you:

I am a visitor to St Davids ☐   I live in St Davids ☐

	Strongly agree	Agree	Neutral	Disagree	Strongly disagree
The town would benefit from more tourists staying overnight					
The proposed hotel would create local jobs					
Other businesses in the town would benefit					

Designing data collection sheets for an Environmental Quality Index (EQI)

Urban fieldwork often involves the collection of environmental evidence. For example, you might want to collect data on:

- safety of the environment (quality of pavements, traffic calming, CCTV);
- pollution (noise, litter, graffiti);
- access (safe places to cross roads, cycle paths, ramps into shops);
- green spaces (amount of vegetation, how well they are maintained and used).

In order to collect this kind of data you will need to design an **environmental quality index (EQI)** sheet. Precise criteria should be used in your sheet. These are statements that are used to quantify each feature of the environment being assessed. This will enable you to get consistent results if several people are collecting the data. Each criterion can then be numbered using, for example, a scale of 1 to 5. This means you can process the data later by calculating means and drawing graphs and maps. An example of this is shown in Figure 21.

It is a good idea to carry out pilot surveys to assess the effectiveness of your EQI sheet before you use it on the fieldtrip. This could be done near to the school, or even in the school grounds, so that the criteria can be discussed with your colleagues. You can then amend the EQI data collection sheet if necessary before the actual fieldtrip.

Don't forget to add the following to your data collection sheet:

- a space to record the location of the survey;
- a space to record the time and date of the survey.

Figure 21 Use precise criteria to assess each feature in an EQI survey.

Feature	Criteria				
	5	4	3	2	1
Vegetation	Plenty of trees. 1+ tree per 20m.	Some trees. 1 tree per 20-39m	Few trees. 1 tree per 40-79m	Sporadic trees. 1 tree per 80-100m.	No trees or greenery.
	5	4	3	2	1
Litter	Occasional litter. One item every 50m+.	Hardly any litter. One item every 11-50m.	Some litter. One item every 6-10m.	Lots of litter. One item every 1-5m.	Abundant litter. More than one item per metre.

Using your phone to measure noise levels

You can use your smart phone to measure noise. You will need to download an App that measures decibels (dB) – there are several free ones available.

Normal conversation is about 65dB. The decibel scale is logarithmic. This means that 75dB is 10 times louder than 65dB and 85dB is 100 times louder than 65dB. Noise on a busy city street will be between 75dB and 85dB.

Adding weightings to an EQI

It is possible that the features included in the survey may not have equal importance. For example, local residents may tell you that they are much more affected by traffic noise and litter than they are by graffiti. If so, you can increase the weighting of the features that are considered to be more important. Do this by multiplying them by a factor, as in Figure 22.

Figure 22 Use weightings to reflect the view that some features of the environment are more important than others.

Feature	Criteria				
	5	4	3	2	1
Vegetation	Plenty of trees. 1+ tree per 20m.	Some trees. 1 tree per 20-39m.	Few trees. 1 tree per 40-79m.	Sporadic trees. 1 tree per 80-100m.	No trees or greenery.
Litter	5x2=10	4x2=8	3x2=6	2x2=4	1x2=2
	Occasional litter. One item every 50m+.	Hardly any litter. One item every 11-50m.	Some litter. One item every 6-10m.	Lots of litter. One item every 1-5m.	Abundant litter. More than one item per metre.
Traffic	5x3=15	4x3=12	3x3=9	2x3=6	1x3=3
	Occasional traffic. Less than 5 cars per minute.	Hardly any traffic. 5-9 vehicles per minute.	Some traffic. 10-15 vehicles per minute. All cars.	Lots of traffic. 16-20 vehicles per minute. Lorries and cars.	Traffic is a nuisance. More than 20 vehicles per minute. Lorries and cars.

Strengths and limitations of EQI surveys	
Some strengths	**Some limitations**
EQIs can include a wide range of environmental factors. They provide quantitative data which can easily be presented. Scores collected by different groups of students can be averaged to improve reliability. Precise criteria for each feature will increase reliability and comparability of results. If EQIs are collected along a transect, trends over distance can be analysed. If EQIs are collected at different places (in two dimensions) the numbers can be mapped and spatial patterns can be analysed.	Scores given may be affected by the time of day, week, or year. Scores for each feature will be inconsistent if groups of students who are using the EQI haven't agreed the criteria carefully first.

Activities

1 **Study Figure 21.**
   a) Explain why the scoring gives 5 marks for 'plenty of trees' and the same score for 'occasional litter'.
   b) Write a set of criteria for:
      i) Graffiti/vandalism
      ii) Condition of pavements
      iii) Access to shops/services
   c) Explain why graffiti/vandalism, condition of pavements and access to shops might be considered to be useful indicators of the quality of an urban environment.

2 **Study Figure 22.**
   a) Describe how you might use a pilot survey to decide how to set these weightings.
   b) Explain why weightings like these are useful.

Collecting qualitative data - making images during fieldwork

You can collect images as evidence of your fieldwork by:

■ taking photographs;

■ making field sketches. These are simple outline drawings of the landscape;

■ creating sketch maps. These are simple maps of the area in which you do your fieldwork. They do not need to be to scale.

Each of these images can be labelled or annotated later when you are analysing your evidence (see page 32).

You might also take video during your fieldwork to collect evidence of, for example:

■ the complex way that people move through pedestrianised streets;

■ the ebb and flow of traffic during rush hour.

The evidence shown in photographs, videos, or sketches is a form of **qualitative data**.

When should images be taken?

If you decide to make images during your fieldwork it is important that you make sure that each image serves a purpose. For example, you might:

■ use an image to provide an overview of the main features of the study area. Field sketches and sketch maps are particularly useful for this because you can concentrate on just showing the main features of the landscape that are relevant to your fieldwork;

■ take a photograph to illustrate the way that data has been sampled. You may be able to annotate this image to analyse the strengths and limitations of the data collection technique;

■ take a series of photographs to provide evidence of individual features that are relevant to your fieldwork. For example, you might want to take photographs of the features that people have identified as being important in a questionnaire or longer interview.

http://www.gridreferencefinder.com/ Use this simple website to find six figure grid references for your fieldwork locations and photos.

Dos and don'ts of taking photos

Do:	Don't:
Provide a reference for the location of any photo that you take for your investigation. An OS grid reference is often best. See the web link above.	✗ Take photographs unless you can analyse them or use them somehow. You are not going to make a scrapbook.

Why draw a sketch map of your fieldwork area?

It might be easy to download a map of your fieldwork area from a website. However, these maps are often cluttered and may be difficult to use. You might decide to use a sketch map instead because you can:

- leave out unnecessary details;
- just include the main features;
- label the features that are important to your fieldwork.

Figure 23 A sketch map of a fieldwork location can focus on just the essential features. This example shows a potential fieldwork location in Central Cardiff.

Figure 24 Apps on your smart phone can be used to record date, location, and altitude. This is the building site shown in the centre of Figure 23. An altitude app on the smart phone used the phone's camera and recorded altitude and location in the bottom left of the photo.

Dos and don'ts of making sketch maps

Do:

✓ Give your map a heading, a north arrow and an approximate scale line.

✓ Make a key to match any colours or symbols on your map.

Don't:

✗ Add too many details and clutter the map.

Activities

1 **Figure 23 was created at the postcode CF10 1EP.**
   a) Use a search engine to find a map of this postcode and its surroundings.
   b) Compare the search engine map to the sketch in Figure 23. What features have been left out of the sketch? Suggest why this make the sketch more useful.
2 **Suggest why it is important to record time, location and altitude as evidence when making a fieldwork image.**

Field sketches

Making a **field sketch**, like Figure 26, is another useful way to collect qualitative data. A field sketch should be used to record evidence about the most important features of a fieldwork location. Focus on drawing just the important geographical features. Leave out anything that isn't relevant. You should add notes to the sketch straight away while you are still in the field, for example:

- a grid reference to locate the sketch;
- labels for the main features;
- more detailed notes (annotations) that help to make sense of the features in your sketch.

Figure 25 Photo of a river cliff on the River Onny in Shropshire.

An overhang at the top of the river cliff has been formed by erosion at the base of the cliff.

Layers of sediment in the cliff is evidence of past deposition. The stones are a similar size and shape to those on the bed of the present-day river..

The grass growing in soil that has slumped down when the river eroded the base of the cliff.

1.6m

The river erodes the base of the cliff by the processes of abrasion and hydraulic action.

Figure 26 Annotated field sketch of the river cliff at grid reference 344910.

Dos and don'ts of field sketches

Do:
- ✓ Look at the feature carefully. If it's a small feature, like Figure 25, take measurements while you are there.
- ✓ Include a scale line.

Don't:
- ✗ Include any unnecessary detail or clutter.

Annotation

Annotation means to add text that makes sense of an image. Annotation is more complex than labels which are simple descriptions. Annotations should be used to analyse key features of the image. The analysis should demonstrate your understanding of those features based on the evidence you collect during fieldwork.

You can annotate field sketches and photos of your fieldwork area. Figure 27 gives an example. The photo shows a range of hard engineering strategies that protect the low lying coastal landscape at Sea Palling in Norfolk. The annotations show understanding of how each strategy works. Notice that the annotations are numbered so that the reader is encouraged to read them in sequence. This helps tell the story given by the data.

Figure 27 Use annotations to analyse the evidence in a photograph. Sea Palling, Norfolk.

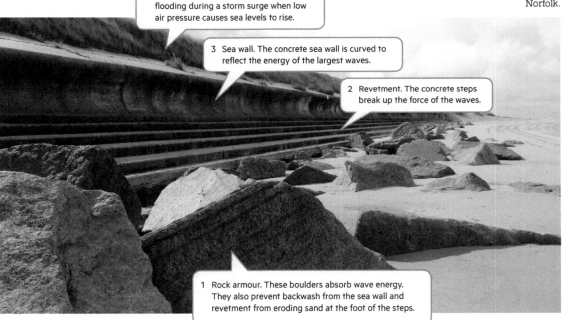

4 The embankment protects the land from flooding during a storm surge when low air pressure causes sea levels to rise.

3 Sea wall. The concrete sea wall is curved to reflect the energy of the largest waves.

2 Revetment. The concrete steps break up the force of the waves.

1 Rock armour. These boulders absorb wave energy. They also prevent backwash from the sea wall and revetment from eroding sand at the foot of the steps.

Strengths and limitations of annotation	
Some strengths	**Some limitations**
Annotation should help you to pick out and analyse the key features of an image quickly and precisely. Annotation can be used to analyse a wide variety of images including photographs, field sketches, and sketch maps.	You may have a limited amount of space for your annotation so choose your words carefully.

Activities

1 **Study the river cliff in Figure 25.**
   a) Suggest an enquiry question or hypothesis that could be investigated in this location.
   b) Design a sampling strategy that would provide further evidence about how the stones in the river cliff were deposited.

Learning objectives
■ Being aware of secondary sources that can be useful in the field.

Using secondary sources to help collect data

A lot of data is available in books and on websites. This is **secondary data** and it can be used at several stages of the enquiry process as shown in Figure 28.

Figure 28 How secondary data may be used in fieldwork

Stage of the enquiry process	How to use secondary data
Planning	Photographs of your fieldwork location from the internet can be used at the planning stage to help you create a hypothesis or pose an enquiry question.
Data collection: Sampling procedures	Tables of data can be used to help you select a sampling strategy. An example is shown on page 37.
Data collection: Collecting qualitative data	Blogs can be used to collect evidence of people's viewpoints.
Data collection: Collecting quantitative data	Many websites contain huge quantities of data. The use of these big data sets is described on pages 36-37.
Data presentation	Tables of data from websites can be used to draw maps and graphs.
Analysis	Websites may include graphs and maps that are relevant to the aims of your fieldwork. Select some and annotate them to help your analysis.

Dos and don'ts of using secondary data

Do:
- ✓ Select secondary data carefully. Only present and analyse data that will be useful to answer your aim.
- ✓ Acknowledge where your evidence has come from. Do this by giving the URL of the webpage where you found the data. Then you will be able to find the source again if you need it.
- ✓ Consider the reliability of the source. Can the evidence be trusted?

Don't:
- ✗ Copy photographs or other evidence from the internet into your portfolio if you don't intend to process or analyse it. You can collect too much stuff which will make your portfolio difficult to work with.

Using your smart phone during fieldwork

Some apps, like the noise meter app described on page 28, turn your smart phone into a measuring tool for collecting primary data. You can also use your smart phone to provide secondary data that may be useful to you while you are working in the field. There are several apps that you might be able to use. Figure 29 shows four of them and suggests how they might be used during fieldwork.

Activities

1 Students wanted to investigate a woodland growing on a hillside. Their enquiry question was *'Are species of tree affected by altitude or angle of slope?'*. The most common trees in the woodland were oak, birch, ash, hawthorn, and holly.
   a) Select and justify a sampling strategy for this enquiry.
   b) Select up to four apps that could be used and explain why you have chosen them.
   c) Design a data collection sheet for use with this enquiry.

Use a plant identification app to help you recognise plants. This might be useful if your enquiry investigated the effects of trampling in an ecosystem such as a sand dune or an urban park.

The iGeology app uses your phone's location to display a geological map of your location. You could use it to see whether local rocks are permeable or impermeable. This might help if your enquiry involves an investigation of flows of water through a drainage basin.

Use an app like this to measure distances, for example, when collecting data along a longer transect (or long profile) through a large town or across a rural area.

There are several apps that will display your elevation above sea level. This could be used to record your height if your transect went up and down a slope. It might also be useful if you were investigating whether land is at risk of flooding. This app will access your phone's camera so you can take images with a record of the time, location and elevation, as in Figure 24 on page 31.

Figure 29 Smart phone apps that you might use during your fieldwork https://www.riverlevels. uk/ This website publishes discharge data for rivers in the UK. You can use it to see how the discharge of a river changes with time. It is too dangerous to collect river velocity data when the river is in flood, so this website is particularly useful for seeing how river discharge changes after heavy rainfall.

https://www.nomisweb. co.uk/census/2011 The official UK National Census website.

Big data

Some websites publish very large databases containing huge amounts of evidence – sometimes known as **big data**. These websites provide secondary data that may be of use to your enquiry. For example, you may be able to find a connection between primary data you have collected and secondary data published on a website:

■ House prices (on a website) might be explained by variations in quality of the urban environment you have found using an EQI.

■ Daily rainfall for the last month (on a website) might help you explain patterns of discharge you have found in a river and its tributary.

The National Census

Sometimes it can be difficult to answer the aims of your enquiry if you are only using primary data. For example, you may need to know such things as:

■ the age structure of the population;

■ the main occupations that people have;

■ how many cars are owned by each household;

■ the level of education that people have achieved.

You might be able to find this data through primary data collection by using a questionnaire. However, this would be very time consuming. Besides, people are sometimes reluctant to talk about their age, their education or their jobs so collecting this as primary data would be tricky. Thankfully, the National Census collects and stores this kind of evidence. It contains information about every household in the UK and includes data about the UK population's age, health, occupations, and education, amongst many other things. The census does have one major limitation: it is a snap-shot in time, recording data every 10 years. Your fieldwork could be located somewhere that has changed significantly since the last census. For example, an enquiry that investigates the sustainability of a new housing estate could not be supported by secondary data from the census if it was built after the census date.

Figure 30 Examples of enquiry questions that would need some secondary data

1 **Are house prices higher closer to the park?**
2 **Is it healthier to live in the suburbs or in the city centre?**
3 **Are fewer crimes recorded in areas that have more CCTV cameras?**
4 **Are the residents of sustainable communities mainly in professional jobs?**
5 **Is car ownership higher in suburbs than in the city centre?**

https://www.streetcheck. co.uk/

This website takes some of the data from the UK National Census and combines it with other big data sets such as data on crime and house prices. It can be searched using place names or postcodes. It provides numbers that you can process. It also presents some data in the form of graphs. You can search the database by postcode. A typical postcode unit (like CF5 2YX) has 200-300 people living in it. A postcode district (like CF5) can have between 8,000 and 85,000 people living in it, depending on whether the area covered by the postcode is rural or urban. It would be SMART to focus your fieldwork enquiry on a small number of postcode units rather than a postcode district which would be too large.

Strengths and limitations of using census data	
Some strengths	**Some limitations**
The census covers the whole of the UK. You can use it to compare data in one neighbourhood to another so you can analyse spatial patterns. The census is repeated every 10 years so you can find evidence of how a place is changing (for example, by comparing data from 2011 with 2001).	Some places change very quickly so the census may not accurately reflect what a place is like on the day of your fieldtrip.

Using census data to select a sample

You can use big data to research your fieldwork location before you visit. For example, you could use the census to decide on a suitable sample of local residents. A suitable sampling strategy for a questionnaire would be a stratified sample – where the number of people in each age group that you interview is in proportion to the actual population. You would do this by completing the following steps.

Step One Use a website with census data. Select the ward and find the population structure data. Figure 31 shows the age structure of Borth, a small seaside town in West Wales.

Step Two Calculate the percentage of people in each age category. For example, to calculate the percentage of people who are over 65 in Figure 31:

Divide 460 by 2,070 (the total) and multiply the answer by 100 = 22.22

This means that, if you questioned 100 people in total, you should interview 22 who are over 65.

Step Three Calculate the number of people to interview if your total sample size is less than 100. So, if you only want to interview 50 people in total, you multiply the answers from Step Two by 0.5 (because 50 is half of 100).

Age of residents	Number of residents in each age group
Over 65	460
30–64	1000
Under 30	610
Total population	2070

Figure 31 The age structure of Borth, West Wales. National Census (2011)

Activities

1 **Use the data in Figure 31.**
    a) Calculate how many people would be interviewed in each age category in a stratified sample of 100.
    b) Calculate how many people would be interviewed in each age category in a stratified sample of 60.
2 **Study Figure 30. It gives examples of enquiry questions which rely on at least some secondary data.**
    Use the street check website to identify at least one type of secondary data that you could use to help you answer each of these enquiry questions.

Geographic Information Systems (GIS)

Lots of websites use interactive maps to show geographical data. They are known as **Geographical Information Systems (GIS)**. These maps are built up from a number of different layers. There is usually a simple base map which shows roads and place names. Then, on top of the base map, there are various layers of data that you can toggle on or off so that you can choose which layer to view. The data is often shown using the colour shading technique used in **choropleth maps**. Figure 32 shows one example. This map shows patterns of deprivation (a measure of inequality). Areas coloured blue/green have a better standard of living than the UK average whereas areas coloured red/orange have a lower standard of living than the UK average.

Using GIS to design a sampling strategy

We can use GIS before the fieldtrip while we are planning our aims and sampling strategies. For example, we could use Figure 32 to plan a transect (sampling along a line) from Birmingham's suburbs towards the city centre. We could use the GIS to check that our proposed transect goes through districts with different levels of deprivation.

Using GIS to investigate socio-economic data

We can use GIS as a source of secondary data to support the primary data collected during the fieldtrip. Several GIS websites display data to do with population, crime, health, house prices, or deprivation. This data is about people and the economy so it is sometimes described as socio-economic data. Figure 33 shows a screenshot from a useful GIS where you can explore crime data. Notice that the data is shown in the form of proportional circles. As you zoom in, the circles break up so you can pin-point where the crimes were reported more accurately.

You might be able to use a combination of primary and secondary data (from a GIS) to help investigate the connection between two sets of data. For example, we could investigate whether:
- traffic is busier (primary data) in areas of higher population density (GIS data);
- there are more CCTV cameras (primary data) in areas which have higher crime rates (GIS data);
- house prices are higher (GIS data) in neighbourhoods that have more green spaces (primary data).

Strengths and limitations of using GIS as a source of data	
Some strengths	Some weaknesses
• The data can be trusted because it has been collected by reliable sources. • Complex data has been presented using maps that are easy to understand so you can quickly see spatial patterns.	• GIS uses secondary data that might not be absolutely up to date. • GIS maps use data from areas (or districts) that contain similar numbers of people. These areas can be quite large in rural areas so it is not possible to see data for smaller, local districts such as individual villages.

https://parallel.co.uk/ This GIS maps data such as population density, deprivation, fuel poverty, and air pollution.

Figure 32 A screenshot from parallel GIS. This GIS uses colour shading to show an index of deprivation. The data for each area pops up as the cursor moves over the map.

Figure 33 A screenshot from the police.uk GIS. This shot shows reported crime in Derby.

https://www.police.uk/ This GIS uses an interactive map to represent recent reports of crime.

Activities

1 Suggest three different enquiry questions, or hypotheses, that could be investigated using a combination of primary data and secondary data from one of the GIS maps shown on this page.

Learning objectives
- Knowing when and how to use mean, median, and mode.

What do we mean by average?

Processing your data will allow you to see what the evidence is telling you. One useful processing technique is to find the average. This is a measure of **central tendency**, in other words, the average tells you something about the central point in your dataset. There are three different ways to express an average. These are mean, median, and mode.

Mean

The arithmetic **mean** value of a dataset is found by:

Step One Adding up all the data to find the total.

Step Two Dividing the total value by the number of items of data.

Geographers often use the mean to find the average for discrete or continuous data. It is especially useful if data has been recorded several times and varies a little each time. For example, you might take five wind speed readings at each location (as in Figure 1) and find the mean. The wind may be gusty so each reading is different. By calculating the mean you can average out these variations. Small variations can also be caused by experimental error. For example, you might measure the time it takes for a dog biscuit to float downstream over a length of 10 metres. You might repeat the experiment 5 times and find each reading is slightly different because you didn't stop the stop watch promptly each time. Then you can take the mean to find an average time that reduces the effect of this experimental error.

Figure 1 A student has collected data on wind speeds at three locations on a hillside. The data is shown in the table (values in metres per second).

Site A – lower slope	4.2	3.9	3.7	3.8	4.1
Site B – middle slope	3.9	4.2	4.4	4.2	4.0
Site C – upper slope	4.8	5.1	4.7	4.8	5.2

Median

The **median** is the middle value when all your data is arranged in rank order. Median is a useful measure to use if you have some extreme values in your dataset. The median is unaffected by these extremes so will still give you a fair measure of the central point in your data. To find the median value:

Step One Put the data in rank order.

Step Two The median is the middle value in an odd number of items of data. In Figure 2, the median value in Group A is 5. If you have an even number of items in your dataset, the median is the half way point (mean) between the two middle values in your dataset. In Figure 2, to find the median value of Group B, add 6 to 12. Then divide the answer by 2.

Figure 2 A student has collected data on the length of commute for three groups of workers in an office in Cardiff. The data is shown in the table (values in miles).

Group A	2	2	3	5	5	5	12	23	26	
Group B	1	2	4	4	6	12	18	22	56	103
Group C	1	1	2	3	4	7	8	12	15	43

Mode

The **mode** is the most frequently occurring value in your dataset. Mode is a useful measure of discrete data in a geographical enquiry. For example, you could use mode to describe the average value collected in a bipolar survey, as in Figure 3.

Step One Tally all the times someone chose a particular value in the bipolar survey.

Step Two The mode is the value that has been chosen most frequently.

	2	1	0	-1	-2	
Pavements are in good condition	2	3	5	18	12	Pavements are in poor condition
Cars never park on pavements	5	10	8	6	1	Cars often park on pavements

Figure 3 A bipolar survey was used as part of an enquiry about reducing risk for pedestrians and cyclists in a busy town. 30 people were surveyed. This table shows the total number of people who chose each value on the scale +2 to -2.

Mode can also be used to find a central point in grouped data. For example, imagine a beach survey in which pebbles are measured and put into categories by size, as in Figure 4. The **modal class** is the category that has most pebbles in it.

Pebble size (mm)	Number of pebbles
Less than 50	32
50-60	28
60-70	15
71-90	15
91-120	10

Figure 4 A student measured the length of 100 pebbles at one location on a beach. The data is shown in the table (values in millimetres).

Strengths and **limitations of using averages**	
Some strengths	**Some limitations**
Mean will give a number on a continuous scale. This is useful if you want to process the data further, for example, by adding the mean value to a scatter graph (see pages 65-67). Mode is always a data value and median will be a data value if you have an odd number of items of data. This is an advantage if you want to present findings that make common sense. For example, in a survey of car ownership, you may find that the mean number of cars owned per household is 1.86! It would be more sensible to report that the mode was 2 cars per household.	Mean can fail to represent the central point fairly if the dataset includes some extreme values or a very wide range of values. Median is a better measure if your data includes extremes.

Activities

1 Calculate the mean wind speed at each location in Figure 1.
2 Study Figure 2.
   a) Calculate the mean, median and mode for each group of commuters.
   b) Explain why the mean value does not fairly represent the central point of this data.
3 Study Figure 3. What is the mode for each statement? What does this tell you about this survey?
4 Study Figure 4.
   a) Which size of pebbles is the modal class?
   b) Identify two faults in the data collection sheet.

Measures of dispersion

Dispersion is a description of how your values are spread (or dispersed) through a dataset. The simplest measure of dispersion is **range**. This is the difference between the highest and lowest value in your dataset. This is useful because the range of one dataset may be very different to the range of another, even if the average value of the two datasets is similar. For example, in Figure 5, quadrats have been used to sample pebbles at two different locations on a beach. The table shows the length of 15 pebbles sampled from each quadrat. The range in values is quite different even though the median is the same. This suggests that wave action has moved pebbles up and down the beach and has sorted them by size – leaving pebbles with a very narrow range of sizes further up the beach.

Figure 5 Pebble sizes at two locations on Vik beach, Iceland.

Length of pebbles (mm)	
Quadrat 1	Quadrat 2
95	25
60	22
35	20
30	20
20	18
18	15
14	14
14	14
11	12
10	11
9	10
9	9
8	9
8	7
7	8

Figure 5.1 Quadrat 1. Pebbles close to the water's edge.

Figure 5.2 Quadrat 2. Pebbles 5 metres from the water's edge.

Interquartile range

The **interquartile range** is another way of measuring the spread of values in a dataset. The interquartile range is the difference between values that are one quarter and three quarters through the dataset so it excludes the largest and smallest values. It is used when the overall spread of values is rather large. To find the interquartile range:

Step One Put the values into rank order and identify the median value. In Figure 5 it is in the green cell.

Step Two Identify the lower and upper interquartiles. The lower quartile is the mid-value between the lowest value in the dataset and the median. It is in the orange cell in Figure 5. The upper quartile is the mid-value between the median and the highest value and the dataset. It is in the yellow cell in Figure 5.

Step Three Calculate the interquartile range by subtracting the value of the lower quartile from the value of the upper quartile.

Dispersion graphs

The range of values in a dataset can be presented visually using a **dispersion graph**, like Figure 6.2. Figure 6.2 shows the range in house prices in Borth, a seaside town. To make a dispersion graph:

Step One Set out your categories of data on the horizontal axis. In Figure 6.2, these are different locations within Borth.

Step Two Mark the vertical axis with a range of values for your data. In Figure 6.2, this is house prices. The highest value is £380,000 so the axis is marked at £50,000 intervals up to £400,000.

Step Three Plot each value in your dataset as a small vertical cross. In this case, each cross represents the value of one house that is for sale in Borth.

Figure 6.1 Borth in West Wales.

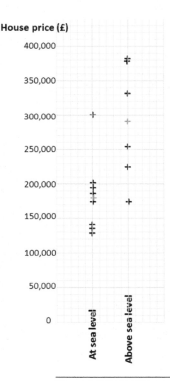

Figure 6.2 Dispersion graph showing range of house prices in Borth (2017).

Activities

1 **Study Figure 5.**
   a) For each quadrat, calculate the:
      i) range ii) median iii) interquartile range
   b) What conclusions can you draw from these results?

2 **Study Figure 6.2.**
   a) What do the red crosses on this graph represent?
   b) Use the graph to calculate the interquartile range in house prices for these two locations.

Types of graph

Graphs are a way of presenting your data in a visual form. They make it easier to see patterns or trends within your data. They also make it possible to compare data easily.

There are lots of different types of graph you can draw but choosing which graph to draw is not just about personal taste. There are some rules about which graphs you can use.

Two of the most common graphs are:

■ **Line graphs** which are used to present continuous data and can be used for discrete data.

■ **Bar charts** (or column graphs) which are used to present discrete data and must **not** be used for continuous data.

Bar charts and line graphs each have two axes. The horizontal axis is known as the x-axis and the vertical axis is the y-axis The place where the two axes meet is called the **origin** of the graph..

Line graphs

Line graphs are used to present continuous data. **Continuous data** is data that is measurable and the result may be recorded to one or more decimal places. Distance, height, slope angle, sound level, velocity (for example, flow of a river or wind speed) and time are all examples of continuous data collected in fieldwork. Figures 9 and 10 each show continuous data displayed as line graphs.

Discrete data in one category, such as the amount of traffic, can be shown as a line graph if the x-axis shows time (for example, in hours, days, or years). Figure 7 shows an example. However, you should never present separate categories of data, such as different shop types, joined by a line.

Time	Pedestrians
8:00	36
8:30	78
9:00	69
9:30	43
10:00	44
10:30	53
11:00	57

Figure 7: Pedestrians in Cardiff Students collected data on pedestrian flows in a busy shopping street. They counted the number of pedestrians who passed by in three minutes every half an hour.

The x-axis of a line graph can be used to show distance along a transect. For example, you can present the slopes of a beach profile as a line graph (see pages 20-21). Figure 10 shows the height of plants growing on a transect that cuts at right angles across a footpath. Cross sections, such as the shape of a river channel, can also be presented as a line graph.

Learning objectives

■ How to choose the right kind of graph for discrete and continuous data.

■ How to present data using a line graph.

Activities

1 Discuss why it is important to start a line graph on the y-axis.

2 Suggest one strength and one limitation of using the y-axis to represent height in Figure 9.

Notice that the line starts on the y-axis. There is no gap.

Figure 8 Students collected data on flows in this rural honeypot site. They set up one transect up the west facing slope, from top to bottom. They collected wind speed data. They also set up a short transect across the footpath to see how plants were affected by trampling. Shropshire Hills, AONB.

Figure 9: Wind speeds
Line graph of wind speeds. Notice that the graph shows height of the hill on the y-axis.

Figure 10: Plant height
Cross section across the footpath showing plant height

Bar charts

You should choose to use a bar chart if you have discrete data. Discrete data is data that can be counted and the result is a whole number. The number of pedestrians in a shopping area and the number of cars passing in 5 minutes are both examples of discrete data. The number of items in a category, for example, the number of pebbles of a particular shape, is another example of discrete data. If the bars are drawn vertically as columns, then the x-axis is used for the categories of data and the y-axis is used for the values. For example, traffic can be shown as vertical bars with different categories of vehicle on the x-axis. Bar charts clearly show the category with the largest and smallest values so are useful for comparing your categories.

Hints and tips for creating bar charts

- It is possible to draw horizontal rather than vertical bars. There is no rule to decide whether your bars should be vertical or horizontal but if your category names are very long then it is easier to label horizontal bars.
- Some categories have a logical sequence and should be shown in the correct order, like Figure 13. However, if your categories have no particular sequence then you can put your data in rank order by value from largest to smallest – making comparison easier. An example is shown in Figure 14.
- Decrease and increase can be shown by using positive and negative numbers on either the x-axis (like Figure 15) or the y-axis (if you want a column graph).

Figure 11 Students collected data in this district shopping centre in Cardiff.

Figure 12 Students recorded shop type on each side of the street. They compared their results to images on Google Street View in 2008 (secondary data).

Shops in Cowbridge Road East	2008	2016
Food shops	2	6
Newsagents	1	1
Cafes/pubs/take aways	20	26
Estate agents	2	3
Health care/chemists	6	2
Furniture / home ware	5	3
Clothes	5	4
Electronics	1	1
Hair salon/beauty	2	2
Charity shops / betting / amusements	10	18
Vacant shops	9	2

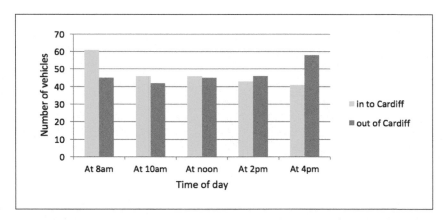

Figure 13 Traffic data was collected in the street shown in Figure 12. Vehicles were recorded travelling in each direction for 3 minutes. The results are presented in a vertical bar (or column) chart.

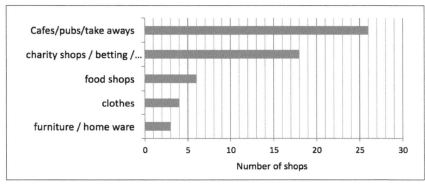

Figure 14 The five most common shop types in 2016 are presented in this bar chart.

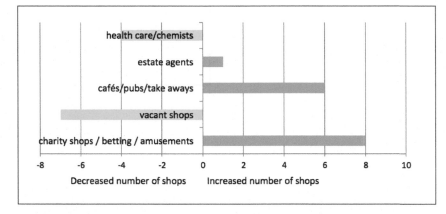

Figure 15 The change in the number of shops in selected categories between 2008 and 2016 is shown in a bar chart that has an x-axis with both positive and negative numbers.

Activities

1 **Study Figure 13.**
   a) Explain why a bar chart has been selected to present this data.
   b) What conclusions can you reach from this data?
2 **Use the data in Figure 12 to practise drawing:**
   a) a horizontal bar chart with the data in rank order;
   b) a vertical bar chart showing the change from 2008 to 2016.

Histograms

A histogram is a type of graph that uses bars. It may look similar to a bar chart but there are some important differences between histograms and bar charts that are shown in Figure 16. Of these differences, the key one is that histograms are always used to represent continuous data. In geography fieldwork, the most common reason to use a histogram would be to represent pebble sizes from a beach, or the sediment sizes sampled from a river.

Bar charts

- Represent **discrete** data (something you have counted) such as types of vehicle in a traffic survey.
- The horizontal axis is used to represent the different categories (for example, cars, lorries, and buses).
- There should be a gap separating each bar.

Histograms

- Represent **continuous** data (something that you have measured). This could be the length of pebbles, the height of plants, or the age of people.
- The horizontal axis is a scale – just like in a line graph. The units of measurement (for example, centimetres) must be shown.
- The bars should touch each other.

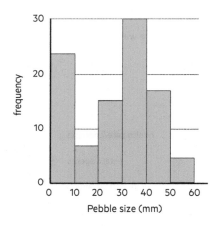

Figure 16 The difference between bar charts and histograms.

Dos and don'ts of drawing histograms

Do:
- ✓ Ensure that the intervals on the horizontal axis are equal in size. This means each bar must be the same width.
- ✓ Use the same scale of horizontal and vertical axis for each of the histograms so you can compare them.

Don't:
- ✗ Use unequal sized intervals.
- ✗ Use different colours for each bar. This may look pretty but it would be misleading. Different colours would suggest that each bar represents something different and these aren't different things – they are all pebbles!

Activities

1 **Study Figure 16.**
   a) How many pebbles are 20-29.9mm long?
   b) Which size of pebbles is the modal class?

Population pyramids

A population pyramid is a type of graph that represents the age structure of a population with bars for males on one side of a vertical axis and bars for females on the other. Age is continuous data so a population pyramid is actually a pair of histograms drawn back-to-back. The most common reason to use a population pyramid during a fieldwork enquiry would be as secondary data. For example, imagine you were investigating the provision of services (education, health, or leisure) in an urban area. A population pyramid could provide evidence of the types of services that the local population might need.

Figure 17 Screenshots from parallel GIS showing two population pyramids from different districts of Huddersfield.

Activities

2 **Study Figure 17.**
   a) Identify two major differences between these population pyramids.
   b) Use the evidence in Figure 17 to suggest which services might be needed in each district.
   c) Suggest how you could use fieldwork to investigate whether local people have fair access to these services.

https://parallel.co.uk/3D/
population-density/
This **GIS** uses two different techniques. It shows population density as a choropleth map. The clever bit is that, as you move the mouse, a population pyramid for that neighbourhood pops up.

Pie charts and divided bars

Pie charts and divided bars are a useful way to present how a whole set of data can be divided up into different parts. Imagine you interviewed 100 people: 15 of them were retired and 12 were students. You could represent this data as a pictogram as shown in Figure 18. However, pictograms like this are time consuming to draw. A simpler and quicker method to show different parts of the whole set of data is to represent each part as a slice of a pie (a sector of a circle).

Figure 18 Pictogram representing the number of retired people and students within a survey of 100 people.

Calculating percentages

To draw a pie chart or divided bar you will need to turn your raw data into percentages. Figure 18 is based on a questionnaire survey of 100 people so the maths is easy – each person is one per cent of the whole. But most data isn't quite as straightforward as this. Look at Figure 19. It shows data from the 2011 census for wards of Newcastle-under-Lyme in Staffordshire. It's an example of raw data – data that hasn't been processed. Notice that each ward has a different total number of residents. Loggerheads has most retired people. It also has more residents than other wards so it's difficult to know whether it has more or fewer retired people than other wards. To make comparisons between wards easier we need to convert this raw data into percentages.

Figure 19 Census data (2011) for selected wards of Newcastle-under-Lyme, Staffordshire.

Location	Ward	Residents	Retired
Inner urban	Town	5,063	467
	Knutton & Silverdale	4,313	439
	Cross Heath	5,887	622
Suburban	Westlands	5,659	792
Rural-urban fringe	Keele	4,129	93
	Loggerheads	6,948	1,068
Newcastle		123,871	14,830

To calculate the percentage of the population of Loggerheads ward that is retired you need to follow these steps.

Step One Divide the number of people in Loggerheads who are retired by the total number of residents in that ward. So, divide 1,068 by 6,948.

Step Two Multiply the answer (from Step One) by 100. So, multiply 0.1537 by 100. The answer is 15.37. This is the percentage of all residents in Loggerheads who are retired.

Step Three You can round the number up or down to the nearest whole number. If the number ends .49 or less, round it down. If it ends .50 or more, round it up. So, 15.37 would round down to 15%.

1 **Study Figure 19.**

a) Calculate the percentage of people who are retired in each ward of Newcastle-under-Lyme.

b) Calculate the percentage of people who are retired in the whole of Newcastle-under-Lyme.

c) Identify one anomaly in the data. Use the internet to research the anomalous ward and explain it.

d) What conclusion can you reach about the data in Figure 19?

Using pie charts and divided bars

To draw a pie chart by hand you will need a pie chart scale or a protractor. A complete pie represents 100% and a circle is divided by 360 degrees. So, to draw a pie chart using a protractor follow these steps.

Step One Calculate your percentages and check they add up to 100%.

Step Two Multiply each percentage by 3.6. For example, to make a sector of a pie for retired people in Loggerheads, multiply 15 by 3.6. The answer is 54. This is the number of degrees for the sector of the pie.

Step Three Draw a line from the centre of the circle to the top (at twelve o'clock if it were a clock face). Then measure around 54 degrees in a clockwise direction and draw a line from the centre to the edge of the circle. This is your first sector. Colour and label it.

Divided bars are even easier to draw and read. Simply draw a bar that is exactly 100mm long so that each 1mm length of bar equals 1 per cent.

Pie charts and divided bars are useful for presenting data where only a few 'parts' make up the whole. Figure 20 shows how effective they can be for making comparisons – in this case, between two different wards. Pie charts are much less effective if they have a large number of sectors.

Figure 20 These pie charts and divided bars represent the data for Loggerheads and Keele.

Retired population of Loggerheads

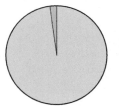

Retired population of Keele

Strengths and limitations of pie charts and divided bars	
Some strengths	**Some weaknesses**
• Pairs of pie charts, each with 2-5 sectors (or slices), are easy to compare. • Pie charts can be located on a map to show spatial patterns (see pages 54-55). • Pies and divided bars simplify complex raw data into simple percentages so they are great ways to show differences and similarities between data when the raw data is of different sizes.	• Some people find pie charts difficult to read. Remember that a sector that is a quarter of the circle is 25% and a sector that is half the circle is 50%. • Don't use a pie chart if you have too many sectors because people find it hard to judge the size of a small slice and lots of different coloured slices means your key will be complex.

Learning objectives

■ How to avoid common mistakes when drawing graphs.

Graphs: getting the details right

It is important to get the details right so that people who view your graph can fully understand what it is telling them about the data. A good graph, selected carefully to make sure it is appropriate for the data (discrete or continuous), will have:

■ a Title;
■ Labels on both the x-axis and y-axis;
■ a Key, if you have used colours or symbols;
■ been drawn neatly and accurately with a ruler.

Figure 21 This graph contains some errors. Compare it to Figure 7 on page 44

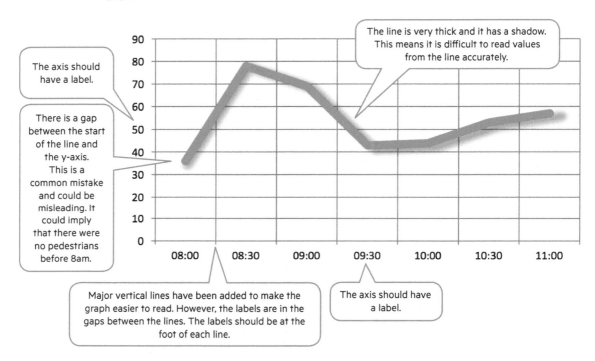

The line is very thick and it has a shadow. This means it is difficult to read values from the line accurately.

The axis should have a label.

There is a gap between the start of the line and the y-axis. This is a common mistake and could be misleading. It could imply that there were no pedestrians before 8am.

Major vertical lines have been added to make the graph easier to read. However, the labels are in the gaps between the lines. The labels should be at the foot of each line.

The axis should have a label.

Dos and don'ts of drawing graphs

Do:

✓ Label each axis and check that you have included the unit of measurement (for example, cm or m/s) in your label.

✓ Start the origin of the y-axis at zero unless you have a good reason not to.

Don't:

✗ Include a gap between the start of a line graph and the y-axis.

Misleading graphs

A good graph allows you to see the data clearly. If the graph is badly drawn it could be misleading – making it difficult to see patterns or make comparisons. One common mistake is to provide a false origin for the y-axis – in other words, one that does not start at zero. Study Figure 22. This pair of graphs shows what happens if the y-axis does not start at zero. Students had collected data on pedestrian flows in a busy shopping street. The left hand graph gives the impression that more than twice as many pedestrians were seen at site B than at site C. However, the y-axis starts at 60 not zero, so differences in height between the bars has been exaggerated. In the right hand graph the y-axis starts at zero. You can see that site A has more pedestrians than B, and B has more than C. However, the differences are actually quite small.

Figure 22 Misleading bar charts

Pictograms

Pictograms are simple pictures that are used to represent quantities. The picture is drawn in proportion to the quantity it represents. Study Figure 23. On the left the pictogram is drawn correctly. Each pictogram represents 10 cars, so location A had 45 cars. On the right the pictogram is drawn incorrectly. The value is 3 times greater so the car has been enlarged until it is 3 times its original length. However, this is misleading. The car is also 3 times its original height. This means the pictogram is actually nine times larger than the original pictogram, suggesting that it represents 90 cars rather than 30.

Figure 23 Misleading pictograms

Drawing maps

Geographers are interested in spatial patterns. These are patterns that exist in two dimensions so they can be represented on a map. Can you represent some of the evidence from your fieldwork on a map? You can use either primary or secondary data to draw your map.

Desire line maps

A **desire line** map uses thin straight lines to show how places are linked together. In geography fieldwork they are often used to show the movement of people, for example, commuters travelling to and from work or visitors to a honeypot site. To draw desire lines you need to know exactly where each line begins so you need to ask the commuter or visitor the name of their home town rather than the name of a county.

Step One Download or sketch a map to use as a base map.

Step Two Plot a straight line for each item of data. In Figure 24, the line should begin where the visitor lives and end at the location of the honeypot site.

Step Three Give your map a **scale line** and north arrow. This is essential so you can describe the pattern made by the desire lines.

Figure 24 A desire line map showing visitors to Dovedale. The area coloured green shows the Peak District National Park.

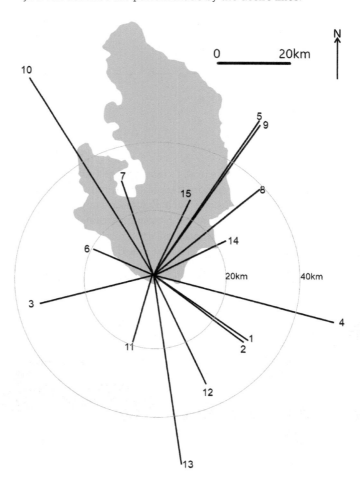

Flow line maps

A **flow line map** uses proportional arrows to show flows, for example, flows of traffic or the movement of pedestrians. The width of each arrow is in proportion to the value of the flow. Proportional arrows can be used to show:

- ■ flows from an area (such as a county) or a place (such as a town);
- ■ data that has an amount and direction but where you don't know where the movement began (for example, traffic on a road).

Step One Draw a simple base map.

Step Two Create a scale for the width of your arrows. This needs to be small enough so that your largest arrows will fit on the map.

Step Three Draw each arrow onto the base map so that they point in the direction of flow. The width of the arrows should be in proportion to the data.

Step Four Add a scale line, north arrow, and key to your map.

Figure 25 Proportional arrows show the number of people walking on footpaths in Dovedale, Derbyshire.

Dot maps

A **dot map** uses individual dots to show the exact location of similar features on a map. It is an effective way to show distribution patterns of **discrete data** (objects that can be counted). In fieldwork, you could use a dot map to show the distribution of services such as schools, post offices, cash point machines, or libraries across a town or rural area. You could also use a dot map to show the distribution of features that are designed to make our urban places safer such as CCTV cameras, speed bumps, or pelican crossings.

Figure 26 shows a dot map of cash points. Notice the cluster of overlapping dots in the town centre. This cluster spreads out as you zoom into the map on screen. This is an issue to be aware of when you draw your own dot map. If some dots are clustered into the same part of the map, it may be better to draw a proportional circle map instead – see page 58.

To draw a dot map plot a dot for each item of data (for example, each CCTV camera or cash point machine) onto a base map. The dot must go in exactly the right location. Use something like a fine tipped felt pen so that the dot is nice and clear but not too large.

https://www.link.co.uk/consumers/locator/ This interactive site allows you to search for cash points by postcode. It creates a dot map.

Activities

1 Identify one strength and one limitation of dot maps.

Figure 26 A dot map showing the location of cash points. Use the web link to create a similar map for your own town.

Isoline maps

An **isoline** is a line on a map that joins places that have an equal value. In fieldwork about spheres of influence you could create an isoline map to show noise levels around a building site, stadium, or busy road.

To draw an isoline map you will need lots of points across a map where data has been collected. Once you've got enough data you can draw the map – a bit like a dot to dot map. However, you also need to be able to **interpolate** - which means to find values that lie between other values.

Study Figures 27 and 28. Each dot on Figure 27 represents a place where data has been collected. The students visited each place and gave a score (out of 5) for the amount of litter that they could see. A value of 5 means lots of litter (either in a bin or on the street) and 0 means there was no litter.

Study Figure 27. There are 5 places where a value of 2 was recorded. We could join them up but it would be easier if there were more points. To create more points we need to interpolate. Each of the red dotted lines has been drawn between values where 2 should be somewhere on the line. Using this method gives us another 5 places that have a value of 2.

Figure 28 shows how to interpolate the data and draw an isoline for 2. Everywhere inside this line has more litter. Everywhere outside this isoline has less litter – it effectively shows a sphere of influence.

A value of 2 must lie half way between the points where 1 and 3 were observed. This is interpolation.

Figure 27 Interpolation of extra data points with a value of 2.

An isoline has now been plotted. It passes through data points with a value of 2 and also through the points we have interpolated.

There must be a value of two part way along each of the red lines.

Figure 28 An isoline with a value of 2 has now been plotted

Activities

2 Make a copy of the data points in Figure 27. Use the interpolation technique to draw an isoline for the value of 4.

Part 1 The enquiry process

Proportional symbols

A **proportional symbol map** uses symbols (usually squares or circles) of different sizes to represent the data. The larger squares/circles represent larger data values – it is the area of the symbol that is in proportion to the value.

Proportional symbols are quite tricky to draw. If your range of data is small, an alternative technique is to draw located bars on a map like Figure 29. However, located bars have a disadvantage - as data values increase, a bar chart gets taller and the largest data needs very tall bars that would be difficult to fit on the map. Proportional symbols also get bigger as data values increase but, because it is their area rather than their height that shows the increase, they remain compact enough to fit on the map - so proportional symbols are useful if you have a large range in your data.

Figure 29 Located bars on a map representing bipolar scores.

Strengths and limitations of proportional symbols	
Some strengths	**Some limitations**
• Proportional symbols are useful if you have a large range in your data.	• It is difficult to estimate the size of a proportional symbol by eye – people underestimate their size.

Activities

1 **Evaluate Figure 31. Identify at least one strength and one weakness.**
2 **Explain why the car park spaces data are best shown using proportional symbols rather than located bars. Use evidence from Figure 30 to support your answer.**

How to draw proportional symbols

To draw a proportional square or circle you need to follow these steps.

Step One Calculate the square root of each piece of data. Put the number in to a calculator and press this √ button. Add your answers to a table like Figure 30.

Step Two Decide on a scale for the symbols. The square root for Raven Meadows is 29.3. A simple scale would be 1:1 so, for Raven Meadows, you would draw a square with a side that is 29mm long, or a circle with a radius of 29mm. If this scale doesn't work well you could consider halving (to make all symbols smaller) or doubling (to make all the symbols larger) all of the square root numbers in your table.

Step Three Download or sketch a simple map that can be used as a base map.

Step Four Draw each symbol. The centre of each symbol should be located carefully in the right place. It is ok to overlap symbols.

Step Five Draw two symbols of different sizes at the edge of your map to make a scale. Use whole numbers that are close to the top and bottom of your range of data.

Step Six Give your map a scale line and north arrow.

https://en.parkopedia.co.uk/ Use this GIS to find the number of parking spaces near to your fieldwork site.

Car park	Number of spaces	Square root √
Saint Austin's Street	48	6.9
Raven Meadows	856	29.3
Saint Julian's Friars	272	
Wyle Cop	240	
Frankwell Main	720	
Shrewsbury Station	189	

Figure 30 Number of parking spaces available in Shrewsbury (2018).

1. Bridge Street
2. Raven Meadows
3. St Julian's Friars
4. Wyle Cop
5. Frankwell
6. Shrewsbury Station

Figure 31 Proportional squares showing number of parking spaces available in Shrewsbury (2018).

Chapter 4

How can evidence be analysed?

https://www.riverlevels.uk/esk

What is analysis?

Analysis is like detective work. You have collected a lot of data. Now you need to sift through this data carefully, selecting the evidence that reveals connections, patterns, or trends. This process will allow you to make sense of the data.

Like a detective, you will need to examine a variety of evidence. You may have collected evidence in the form of tables of data, photographs, interviews, graphs, charts, or maps. The techniques that will help you make sense of this evidence are described in this chapter.

As you begin to analyse your data it might be helpful to ask yourself some questions. For example:

- *Do I have any evidence for ...?*
- *Why do I think that...?*
- *How clear is the pattern or trend?*
- *How strong is the connection between this variable and that?*
- *What may be causing this variation in the data?*
- *What effect does this variable seem to have?*

Three key points

A simple technique that you can use with almost any kind of evidence is to identify the three key points that the data is telling you. If you are making sense of a graph or a table of data you might look for:

- the overall trend – is it going up or down?
- the range – the difference between the highest and lowest values;
- any values that don't fit the overall trend. We call these anomalies.

Figure 1 shows an example of a hydrograph. This is a line graph that shows how the amount of water in a river changes over time. If you want to challenge yourself:

- try to identify five key points instead of three;
- use descriptive words that describe the patterns or trends you can see. Figure 2 gives examples of useful words to use.

The amount of water fluctuates during the year with many peaks and troughs.

Even during the summer months, the river level fluctuates up and down between about 0.4 metres and 0.7 metres.

The peak discharge (maximum amount of water) was 1.7m in November 2015. Discharge was above 1.5 metres three times during this winter.

River level (m)

1.5

1

0.5

1 Jan 2015   1 Apr 2015   1 Jul 2015   1 Oct 2015   1 Jan 2016

— Typical Low — Measurement

Figure 1 A hydrograph for River Esk in Cumbria. Three key points have been identified.

Clustered	Values (or points on a map) are concentrated into small groups.	**Linear**	Features (on a map or photograph) are spread out along lines.
Decreasing	The values are going down. Add **slowly**, **steadily** or **rapidly** to describe the trend.	**Random**	Values (or features on a map or photograph) are at irregular spaces and show no clear pattern.
Fluctuating	The values in the data vary up and down in a repeated pattern.	**Regular**	Values (or features on a map or photograph) are repeated at even spaces.
Increasing	The values are going up. Add **slowly**, **steadily** or **rapidly** to describe the trend.		

Figure 2 Useful descriptive words to make sense of data

Activities

1 **Add two more key points to Figure 1.**

Text analysis

Text is an important source of evidence. It can provide both facts and opinions. The way that the text is written may tell you something about what somebody thinks of a geographical issue – their perception. You may have collected text as part of your evidence if you have interviewed people or asked open questions in a questionnaire. You may also have collected text evidence from books, newspapers, or the internet in the form of:

- blogs;
- interviews;
- adverts;
- news articles;
- reviews.

Simple ways to analyse text

How do you analyse any patterns or trends when your evidence is in words? There are a number of simple things you can do.

1   Use one colour of highlighter to identify facts and another colour to identify opinions. In Figure 4, one fact has been highlighted in yellow in interview 1. One opinion is highlighted in green.

2   Consider the tone of the text – what kinds of words are used? Are the words mainly positive or is a negative tone used in some of the text? You can count the words or phrases that have a positive tone and then compare those words/phrases that have a negative tone in a bar chart. In Figure 4, one positive phrase has been highlighted in pink in interview 2. One negative phrase is highlighted in blue.

3   Copy and paste your text into an online tool that counts the frequency of words that are used. The text of the interviews in Figure 4 has been analysed in this way and the top 20 words used in each interview are shown in Figure 5. You can analyse these lists. Are the words mainly nouns that identify physical features of the environment, or human features? Are there many adjectives? The number of times that adjectives such as 'beautiful', 'pretty' and 'friendly' can be graphed using a bar chart. This will tell you something of the positive (or negative) perception of a place.

Activities

1   **Analyse the text in Figure 4.**
   a) Identify one fact and one opinion in each interview.
   b) Count the number of times that each interview describes:
      i)   a physical feature of the environment;
      ii) a human feature of the environment.
   c) What are the main similarities and differences between Interviews 1 and 2? Use evidence from Figures 4 and 5. You could draw bar charts to help this analysis.
2   **Describe how the interviews in Figure 4 could be used as a pilot survey to create a more closed qualitative survey. See page 23 to help your answer.**

Figure 3 Borth, a small seaside town in west Wales.

Interview 1 Borth is a small seaside town in West Wales. It is a wild and natural place that is close to nature. The estuary is constantly changing: the light shines on the water and reflects off pools of water on the beach. Birds soar in the sky above. This place is magical. It's as though the landscape is alive. The light is beautiful. I think it's because the weather changes so much and we have light that reflects off the estuary and the waves. The beach is glorious. When the tide is out a long way the wet sand glistens and shines in the light. The sand is soft and clean. I think the beach is really beautiful. I love walking along the pebbles looking for things that have been washed up in the tide. The beach is a lovely place but it can be wild in the winter when the storm waves crash against the pebbles. Then you know that nature can have wild forces.

Interview 2 Borth is a friendly place. Local people are very friendly and want to help. I like the main street with its cheap cafes and shops selling holiday souvenirs. You can get most things in the local shops but not everything so we have to drive quite a long way to do some shopping - like clothes. The main street has pretty little cottages on either side. Some of the old cottages are made out of pebbles off the beach. The town has a lot of interesting history. There are special legends about the place too - legends about the sea and the drowned forest. I think the history of the place is very interesting. Borth is pretty in the summer and the beach is beautiful but it can be rather bleak here in the winter and sometimes I feel quite isolated.

Figure 4 Transcripts of two interviews. Students were investigating the concept of place in Borth. They interviewed visitors and recorded what they said about the place

Interview 1		Interview 2	
Primary words	Frequency	Primary words	Frequency
light	4	place	3
beach	4	legends	2
place	3	history	2
wild	3	beach	2
pebbles	2	cottages	2
sand	2	pretty	2
beautiful	2	shops	2
water	2	main	2
nature	2	Borth	2
estuary	2	friendly	2
shines	2	local	2
reflects	2	very	2
think	2	street	2
waves	2	quite	2
tide	2	interesting	2
glorious	1	isolated	1
much	1	sometimes	1
weather	1	old	1
landscape	1	beautiful	1
magical	1	cafes	1

http://www.textfixer.com/tools/online-word-counter.php

Figure 5 Text analysis of the two interviews to identify the most frequently used words

Making connections

To make sense of your data you also need to make connections between the evidence. Looking for evidence of cause and effect will help you to explain the evidence. For example, imagine an investigation of the shopping centre shown in Figure 6. You might investigate the patterns of pedestrian flows. Why are some parts of the town centre busier than others? You could collect evidence such as:

■ pedestrian surveys at different times of day;
■ interviews with shoppers about the features of the town centre that they like and dislike;
■ the rateable value of shops could be found on the internet.

To make sense of this evidence you might look for connections such as:

■ whether the busiest streets also have a lot of features that the shoppers like;
■ whether rateable values are higher in the busiest streets. If so, this might explain why national chain stores are located on busy high streets but local shops are on quieter side streets.

Figure 6 Why is this shopping street particularly busy? Shrewsbury.

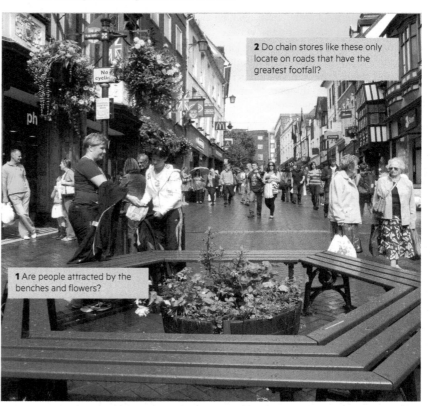

2 Do chain stores like these only locate on roads that have the greatest footfall?

1 Are people attracted by the benches and flowers?

Activities

1 a) **Suggest three different reasons why some shopping streets have more pedestrians (footfall) than others.**
  b) **Identify the data that you would need to collect to investigate the reasons for variations in footfall in a busy shopping street.**

Scatter graphs

A **scatter graph** is a type of graph that is used to show the possible connection (or correlation) between two sets of data. To draw a scatter graph you will need **bivariate data**. That is two sets of data (or variables) that you think may be connected in some way.

Step One Think about how the two variables may be connected. For example, in Figure 7, a student has collected data from the Census about the educational background and occupations of people living in 14 different neighbourhoods in Cardiff. The student thinks it is likely that more people will have professional occupations in wards where more people have a degree. If so, the percentage of people in professional occupations will be the **dependent variable** because the value of this number will depend on the percentage of people who have degrees – not the other way around.

Step Two Draw a pair of axes. The dependent variable should go on the vertical axis. The **independent variable** – in this case the percentage of people with a degree – should go on the horizontal axis. Try to make the two axes about the same length as each other so that the finished graph is square. This will make it easier to see any patterns on the graph.

Step Three Label each axis.

Step Four Plot the points for each ward onto the graph. Vertical crosses are the best way to plot each point. These will line up with the vertical and horizontal grid lines on your graph paper – so your plots should be accurate and easy to read.

Step Five Calculate the **mean (M)** value for each variable. Plot this point onto your graph – perhaps using a different style or colour so that it stands out from the other points on the graph.

Step Six Draw a line of best fit on your graph. The line must pass through the mean value (M). It should also follow the trend of the other points – but it doesn't need to go through any of them or join them up. However, there should be the same number of points on each side of the line of best fit. Notice that the line of best fit does not have to go through the **origin** of the graph (see page 67).

How do I tell if there is a correlation?

A scatter graph will show a correlation between the two variables if:

The dependent variable increases as the independent variable also increases. This pattern suggests that there is a **positive correlation** between the two variables. Figure 8 shows an example of a positive correlation.

The dependent variable decreases as the independent variable increases. This pattern suggests that there is a **negative correlation** between the two variables. Figure 9 shows an example of a negative correlation.

There is no correlation between the two variables if the points are scattered across the graph without making any pattern.

Ward	% of residents with a degree	% of residents in professional occupations
Adamsdown	28	14.5
Butetown	33	20.1
Caerau	10	5.4
Canton	50	32.8
Cathays	22	13.4
Ely	9	6.1
Grangetown	22	13
Llanishen	31	19.5
Pontprennau	38	23.8
Rhiwbina	35	27.9
Riverside	32	20.1
Rumney	13	9.2
Splott	26	17
Whitchurch	37	26.8
Mean	27.57	17.83

Figure 7 Census data for education and occupation in selected wards of Cardiff.

Figure 8 Scatter graph representing the relationship between the bivariate data in Figure 7.

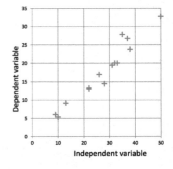

Figure 9 Scatter graph showing a negative correlation.

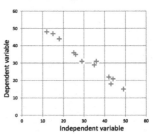

■ Understanding the difference between correlation and causality.

Correlation and causality

Correlation implies that there is some connection between two sets of variables. However, the explanation for this connection may not be clear. For example, in studying the Census data for Cardiff, a student noticed that the percentage of households in inner urban wards who did not own a car was higher than in suburban wards. The student plotted a scatter graph with distance from the CBD on the horizontal axis. The graph showed a negative correlation. However, the explanation for this link is not clear. It could be that:

■ Households in the inner city are poorer and cannot afford a car.
■ Fewer homes in the inner city have driveways so there are fewer places to park a car.
■ People living in the inner city have access to frequent buses and trains so don't need a car.

Causality means that there is a direct link between the two variables. This link can be used to explain why the value of the dependent variable changes. For example, in a study of 20 European cities, a student found a negative correlation between average July temperatures and latitude, that is distance from the Equator.

Activities

1 **Study the list of paired variables in the table below. For each pair state:**
   a) which is the dependent variable and which is the independent variable;
   b) whether you would expect to see a positive or negative correlation;
   c) whether you think the relationship shows correlation or causality. Make sure you can justify each of your decisions.

Fieldwork context	Variable One	Variable Two
A sandy beach	Wind speed (metres per second)	The height that sand is carried (by the wind) above the beach (in centimetres)
A transect up a hillside between 150m and 400m above sea level	Height above sea level (metres)	Wind speed (metres per second)
A pebble beach	The average size of sediment (millimetres)	Distance along the beach – measuring in the same direction as the movement of longshore drift (metres)
An eroded footpath in a honeypot site	Distance from the car park (metres)	Width of the area affected by erosion (metres)
Study of 10 different soil samples	Infiltration rate (cubic cms per minute)	Percentage of the soil composition made of clay particles
The area around a busy main road	Noise levels (decibels)	Distance from the road (metres)
A housing area close to an attractive urban park	Distance from the park (metres)	House prices (£1,000s)
A study of a river channel over several days	The discharge in the river channel (in cubic metres per second)	The amount of rainfall each day (in millimetres)
A larger urban area	Population density (number of people living per km²)	Distance from the city centre (km)
A larger urban area	Population density (number of people living per km²)	The percentage of households who do not own a car

Extrapolation and interpolation

You can use a line of best fit to estimate other values that could be expected if other points followed the same trend. This process is called:

- **Interpolation** if you estimate a value that is within the range of values plotted on your scatter graph. If most points on your graph are close to the line of best fit then interpolation should give a reliable estimate. However, the estimate will be less reliable if some points lie further away from the line of best fit.

- **Extrapolation** if you estimate a value that is outside the range of values plotted on your scatter graph. Extrapolation should give a reasonably accurate estimate if you try to estimate values that are only a little beyond the range of figures on your graph. However, you need to be cautious and consider whether your estimate is realistic. For example, on Figure 10, a ward with 2% of residents with a degree would have a minus figure for residents in professional occupations – this would be impossible!

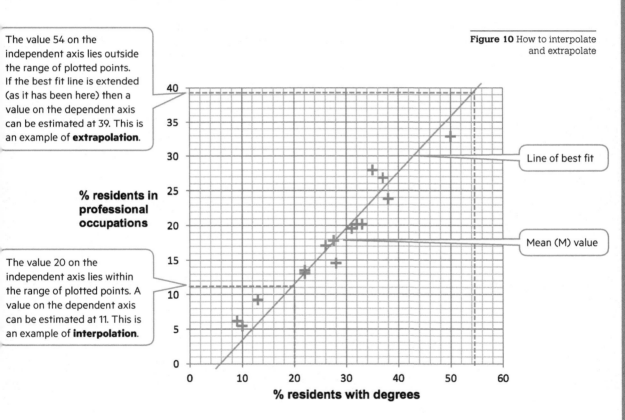

The value 54 on the independent axis lies outside the range of plotted points. If the best fit line is extended (as it has been here) then a value on the dependent axis can be estimated at 39. This is an example of **extrapolation**.

% residents in professional occupations

The value 20 on the independent axis lies within the range of plotted points. A value on the dependent axis can be estimated at 11. This is an example of **interpolation**.

Figure 10 How to interpolate and extrapolate

Line of best fit

Mean (M) value

% residents with degrees

Conclusion

Learning objectives

In this chapter we will explore:

- How to reach conclusions from your fieldwork enquiry.

How to reach a conclusion

You've collected data, processed, presented, and analysed it. It's time to end your enquiry by making your conclusions. A conclusion should make use of the evidence you have collected and analysed. To conclude an enquiry you need to:

1 remind yourself of the enquiry's aims;
2 consider the evidence;
3 draw together your overall findings for each enquiry question or hypothesis;
4 make a judgement/construct an answer to your original aim.

Step One Revisit the aims of the enquiry

It is important to remind yourself of the aims of your enquiry. The aims of an enquiry are often based on your understanding of a geographical issue, concept, or theory. What was the concept that you were investigating? What did you expect to find – did you make any predictions? In your conclusion you need to decide whether or not you have met your aims.

Step Two Consider the evidence

Think about each piece of evidence from primary and secondary sources. Each separate table, graph or map you have drawn is a piece of evidence and each tells a small part of the story. What patterns, trends, and connections can you see?

Step Three Draw together your overall findings

You will need to draw together all of the separate pieces of evidence from your enquiry. It is rather like making a jigsaw puzzle. You need to bring these pieces of evidence together so that you provide an overall conclusion.

Step Four Write your conclusion

When you write a conclusion you should refer to each piece of evidence. Remember to answer each hypothesis. Draw it all together by making a judgement, constructing an answer to your original aim.

Messy geography

The results of your fieldwork will not always be what you expected. When you look at the evidence, graphs may show no real trend and patterns on maps are not always neat and tidy. For example, you might think that a map of house prices for your local town would show that the lowest house prices are close to the town centre. You might also expect that your fieldwork would show that house prices get steadily more expensive as you move out towards the suburbs. If so, a map of house prices would show a regular (or systematic) pattern. In reality, such a map is likely to be much more complex. It is likely to show clusters of higher house prices in inner urban areas – probably connected to positive features of the environment such as urban parks. In reality, the results of geography fieldwork are often messy rather than neat and tidy. Don't be surprised if your results don't exactly match your predictions.

Figure 1 A photograph of the study area. Borth, West Wales

A group of students investigated the effect of new coastal defences at Borth, a small seaside town in West Wales. They wanted to know:

■ whether the coastal defences had positive or negative impacts on the town;

■ how large the sphere of influence might be.

They conducted bipolar surveys to see what positive and negative impacts the construction of the new coastal defences might be. They also collected evidence of house prices to see whether the coastal defences created enough confidence for people to ask high prices for homes that were close to the sea. Their hypotheses were:

■ *House prices are higher closest to the sea.*

■ *Houses at sea level are more vulnerable to flooding (despite the defences) so are worth less than houses above sea level.*

■ *The sphere of influence is affected by height above sea level rather than distance from the sea.*

Two key pieces of evidence are presented in Figures 2 and 3.

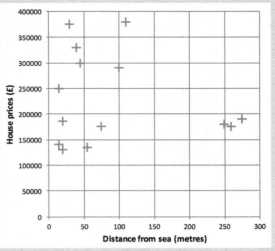

Figure 2 A scatter graph showing the possible relationship between distance from the sea and house prices in Borth

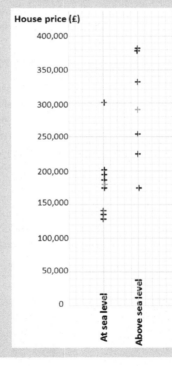

Figure 3 A dispersion graph showing the range of house prices at sea level (less than 3 metres above high tide) and above sea level (on the hillside in Figure 1)

Activities

1 Describe the evidence shown in Figure 2.

2 Use Figure 3 to identify:

   i) the median value of house prices in each location;

   ii) the range of house prices in each location.

3 What conclusion can you draw when you put these two pieces of evidence together? Think about whether the students were able to answer any of their hypotheses.

Chapter 6
Evaluation

Identifying limitations in data

Evaluation is the final stage of the enquiry process. It is an opportunity to weigh up the strengths and weaknesses of what you have done. Your conclusions are based on the data so if there are problems with the data, or faults in the way that data has been collected, then the conclusions could be wrong. That's why it is so important to think critically about whether the data can be trusted.

There are two main types of limitation with data.

Accuracy - how close a measurement is to the actual value (or true value). For data to be accurate it needs the equipment to be used correctly and the result to be recorded carefully in the correct units.

Reliability - how certain you can be that your measurements are true. For data to be reliable it needs to be collected in such a way that, if the fieldwork is repeated, a similar set of data would be collected.

Limitations in primary data

There are a number of reasons why there may be errors in primary data. Accuracy and reliability of data may be affected by:
- errors when you read the apparatus, for example, you are weighing some sediment samples but forget to zero the scales;
- carelessness when the results are recorded. Data errors can be caused by reversing numbers when you write them down. Untidy handwriting can also cause data errors;
- a flaw in the sampling method, for example, you only take one noise reading and it happens to be at a very noisy moment. Wind speed and noise levels vary constantly. You will get a more reliable measure if you take several readings and then calculate the mean.

Figures 1, 2, and 3 give three examples of how data errors can occur and how they can be avoided.

If you are using a ruler to measure the length of a pebble you are relying on your eye to judge where the measurement starts and ends.

Using callipers means you can measure the true value exactly without any guesswork.

Measuring in millimetres is more accurate than measuring to the nearest centimetre.

Figure 1 Use the correct equipment to improve accuracy of data.

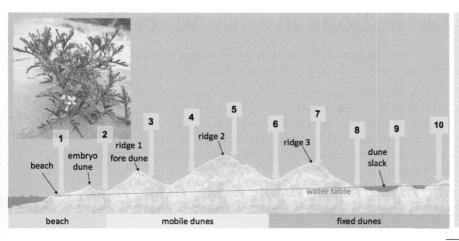

This systematic sample is a suitable technique. However, the transect is about 500m long so there are huge gaps between sample points.

Some variations in data occur over very short distances. For example, sea rocket only grows in the embryo dunes. If regular sample points are too far apart, this important plant will be missed completely.

Figure 2 Use the correct sampling technique to improve accuracy of data.

Reliability is achieved by strictly following the same sampling procedures each time the data is collected. For example, unreliable data would be collected by teams of students if traffic was counted for 3 minutes at 10 locations but:

- the teams had not synchronised their watches so data was not collected at the same time;
- or some teams used stopwatches to keep to exactly 3 minutes but others did not.

Figure 3 Use exactly the same sampling technique as other team members to improve reliability of data.

Dos and don'ts of data recording

Do:
- ✓ Be neat when you write down results in the field. A lot of errors occur because numbers have been written badly and cannot be read later when you get back to the classroom.
- ✓ Check equipment has been zeroed correctly.
- ✓ Take multiple measurements if data is varying.
- ✓ Use exactly the same methods as other team members if you are collecting data in a group.

Don't:
- ✗ Wait until later (for example, after it has stopped raining) to record the data. You will forget the details so do it straight away.

Limitations in secondary data

The accuracy of secondary data may depend on how recently the data was collected. For example, data for the national census is only collected every 10 years.

Some sources and websites are more reliable than others. We can trust that big data collected by a UK government department, or academic organisation, will be reliable because it will have used a suitable sampling method. However, data on some websites may be unreliable because we do not know who collected the data or how large the sample was. There may be **bias** because the website is trying to put across a certain point of view.

Bias

Biased data may be factually incorrect, or its accuracy may be a matter of opinion. This is especially true of qualitative rather than quantitative data. If we analyse the evidence presented to us in the media (on TV, in newspapers, or in blogs) or in qualitative surveys such as questionnaires and interviews, we can identify that some data is presented as fact but is actually biased because it is someone's opinion. Identifying this bias is useful. It helps us describe the opinions of certain groups of people. By considering this bias we may also begin to understand why certain groups of people have strong opinions.

It is important to avoid writing questions that lead people to agree with your own point of view when designing a questionnaire. When you evaluate fieldwork that contains qualitative data collection you need to consider whether your method of data collection led to biased results or not.

Suggesting improvements

As part of your evaluation you should think carefully about whether there is anything else you could have done. A lot of students write that they could have collected more data but think about what kind of data you needed. More of the same data might not have told you anything else. It might be better to think about other kinds of data and the issues you might have had collecting it. For example, could you have:
- asked different questions in a questionnaire?
- collected data at a different time of day?
- collected data at the same time but on another day?
- found some secondary data to clarify an issue where your primary data was inconclusive?

Dos and Don'ts of evaluation

Do:
- ✓ Think about the strengths and weaknesses of your sampling strategy. With hindsight, did you choose the best strategy to give you data that represents the whole?
- ✓ Identify any possible inaccuracy or unreliability. Suggest how you might change the enquiry if you did it again.
- ✓ Identify bias and try to explain why certain groups of people provide biased evidence.

Don't:
- ✗ Simply suggest that you could have done more. A bigger sample might not have given you different results but different questions in your questionnaire might have been more effective.
- ✗ Write about what you enjoyed and didn't enjoy on the fieldtrip. That's not evaluation.

Be SMART

You can evaluate your enquiry using the mnemonic SMART (Specific, Measurable, Achievable, Realistic, Time-based). This technique, shown in Figure 4, can help you evaluate your aims and the design of your sampling techniques.

		5	4	3	2	1	
S	The enquiry had a clear aim and specific focus. I know what I was trying to prove.						The aim was vague. It lacked focus. I didn't know what I was trying to prove or disprove.
M	I could measure all outcomes of the fieldwork. I used a range of techniques to collect qualitative and quantitative data.						I struggled to measure any outcomes of the fieldwork. I wasn't sure which techniques to use.
A	The enquiry was achievable and safe. Primary and secondary data was available to provide the evidence I needed to meet my aims.						There wasn't enough of the right kind of data available to me so I couldn't find the evidence I needed to prove / disprove my aims.
R	The aims were realistic. I had the right data collection skills and accurate equipment.						The aims were unrealistic because I didn't have the right skills or equipment to collect the data I needed.
T	I had enough time to collect data across a range of places / time so that I could see patterns and trends.						I would have needed more time to collect enough data to see any patterns or trends in the data.

Figure 4 Use this SMART bipolar survey to evaluate your enquiry.

These students measured river depth so that a cross section of the channel could be drawn. They measured down from a line that was stretched horizontally across the river channel.

They took depth readings at 1 metre intervals as they crossed the river. They used a rule to take the measurements and recorded the data to the nearest centimetre.

They didn't have any way of checking whether their line was actually horizontal. There was some slack in the line – you can see it in the photo. So, if they had repeated the task they would probably have found some significant variation in their measurements.

Figure 5 How accurate and reliable are the results from this data collection?

Activities

1 **Make a copy of Figure 4.**
   a) Use the bipolar statements to evaluate your own enquiry.
   b) Once you have completed the survey, you could:
      i) explain why one aspect of your enquiry was successful;
      ii) explain why another aspect of your enquiry had limitations;
      iii) suggest and justify how your enquiry could have been improved.
2 **Study the information in Figure 5.**
   a) Describe one strength of this fieldwork.
   b) Suggest one way this fieldwork could be made more accurate and one way it could be made more reliable.

PART 02

Chapter 7
Coastal investigations

Learning objectives
■ How to investigate pebble sorting on a beach.

Investigating coastal processes

In a coastal environment, sediment is transported up the beach in the **swash** each time a wave breaks. It is then transported back down the beach by the **backwash**. Swash can provide a powerful force, moving sand, gravel, and pebbles of all sizes up the slope of the **beach profile**. The backwash usually has less energy. It drags smaller sediment back down the beach profile but larger pebbles are left behind. These larger pebbles sometimes form distinctive ridges near the top of the beach profile.

Figure 1 Swash and backwash on a pebble beach. Llantwit Major, Wales.

Investigating a beach profile

You should start with a hypothesis such as:

'Pebble sizes are larger at the top of the beach profile than at the bottom of the beach profile.'

To investigate this hypothesis you would follow these steps.

Step One Use a clinometer and tape to measure the gradient of the beach profile from close to the water's edge to the top of the beach (see pages 20-21).

Step Two Decide on a sampling strategy for the pebbles. For example, you could collect data from 5 equally spaced sites along the beach profile. This would be a form of **systematic** sampling along a **transect**.

Step Three Measure the length of the same number of pebbles at each site. To be sure that you are observing a real pattern in the data (rather than some pattern that is due to chance) you will need to measure at least 25 pebbles at each site. Do this using a **quadrat** and a set of **random number tables**.

Measuring pebbles

Pebbles are 3-dimensional objects with three axes – each axis is at right angles to the others. To record pebble size and shape you need to measure all three axes as shown in Figure 2. If you just want to record the size of the pebbles you can:

- measure the length of the b-axis only;
- measure all three axes for each pebble and then divide by 3 to get an average.

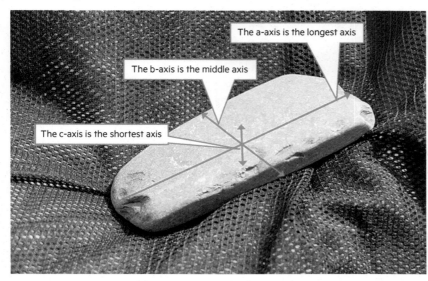

The a-axis is the longest axis

The b-axis is the middle axis

The c-axis is the shortest axis

Figure 2 Each pebble needs to be measured in the same way.

The most suitable and effective way to represent this data would be to draw 5 histograms - one for each site above a line that represents the beach profile. To draw each histogram you will need to follow these steps.

Step One Decide on the intervals for the scale along the horizontal axis of the histograms. To do this, look at the range of data. Let's imagine the shortest pebble was 5mm long and the longest was 50mm long. If so, set out the horizontal axis starting at 0 and ending at 50mm and label intervals every 10mm. Your axis should look like the one in Figure 3.

Step Two Sort your data. Make a tally chart and sort your data into categories. These categories will depend on the intervals you chose in step one. So, how many of your pebbles were between 0mm and 9mm long? How many were between 10mm and 19mm long, etc?

Step Three Draw a bar to represent the number of pebbles in each category. Each bar must touch the next one.

Step Four Give the vertical axis a label. The word **frequency** is often used here – it means the number of times something fell into each category.

Step Five Label the horizontal axis and add the units of measurement – in this case it is mm.

Step Six Give your graph a title. Include the site name (or number) so you know where this data was collected along the beach profile. This is really important if you are going to analyse any patterns and prove (or disprove) your hypothesis.

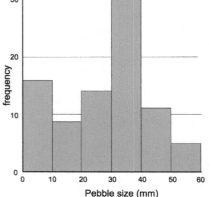

Figure 3 Histogram representing pebble size.

Practice questions

1 Study Figure 4. It shows a possible fieldwork location.

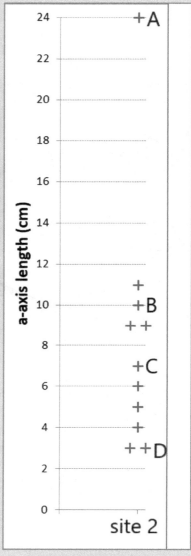

Figure 6 Site 2. Dispersion graph.

1.1 Identify **one** potential risk that could occur while doing fieldwork in this environment. [1]

1.2 Suggest **one** way that this risk could be reduced. [1]

1.3 Identify **one** hypothesis that could be investigated here. [1]

1.4 Identify **two** data collection techniques that could be used to investigate this environment. [2]

1.5 Use the evidence in Figure 1 to complete this annotation by choosing answer a), b), or c). [1]

There is evidence that swash has ...

a) eroded larger pebbles from the upper beach.

b) rolled larger pebbles up the beach.

c) deposited sand on the upper beach.

2 A student measured pebble sizes at two sites: one at the bottom of the beach and the other at the top of the beach. Data for Site 1 is shown in Figure 5. Data from Site 2 is shown in Figure 6.

Figure 5 Site 1. Measurements along the long axis of each pebble.

Pebble	a-axis (cm)
1	18
2	2
3	1
4	6
5	4
6	8
7	9
8	2
9	11
10	2
11	3

Exam advice

In the exam you could be asked to complete a graph, like this dispersion graph, by adding data. Read the axis carefully. You will be marked on the accuracy of your plot.

2.1 Give the median pebble size at site 1. [1]

2.2 Explain why the median is a more useful measure than mean for this data. [2]

2.3 Calculate the interquartile range at site 1. Show your working. [2]

2.4 Match the following features to labels A-D on Figure 6. [4]

Upper quartile   *Maximum*   *Minimum*   *Median*

2.5 Calculate the range at site 2. Show your working. [2]

2.6 The students came to the conclusion that pebbles at the top of the beach are larger than pebbles at the bottom of the beach.

Explain why this conclusion may be unreliable. [2]

3 A group of students measured pebbles at five sites on a beach profile. Their results are shown in Figure 7.

Figure 7 A student photo and histograms

3.1 Suggest a suitable annotation that explains the evidence at A in Figure 7. [2]

3.2 What conclusions can you reach from the evidence in Figure 7? [4]

Investigating coastal management

The risk of coastal flooding is high in some parts of the UK such as the Norfolk coastline shown in Figures 8 and 10. However, coastal management is expensive so we need to assess whether coastlines are worth protecting. We could investigate the potential impacts of coastal flooding using a weighted Environmental Quality Index (EQI) like the one shown in Figure 9. In this EQI the weightings give larger scores for economic flood risks but you could alter these weightings.

Figure 8 The metal flood gates (on the left of the photo) and a large earth embankment at Sea Palling protect homes and businesses in the flat, low-lying coastal areas of Norfolk from coastal flooding.

Economic	Businesses at risk	Large shops or factories at risk	40	Small shops at risk	20	No businesses at risk	0
Economic	Transport links at risk	Major roads or rail lines at risk	30	Minor roads at risk	15	No roads at risk	0
Environmental	Damage to habitats	Rare habitats at risk	10	Mixture of habitats at risk	5	Some low value habitats at risk	0
Environmental	Damage to buildings	Historic buildings at risk	10	Ordinary buildings at risk	5	No buildings at risk	0
Social	Risk to community	Vital services at risk	20	Non-vital services at risk	10	No services at risk	0
Social	Risk to residents	Large population including elderly	30	Small population	15	No local residents	0

Figure 9 A weighted EQI to help assess flood risk.

Hard engineering strategies

Coastal management strategies include hard engineering strategies such as building sea walls, groynes, or the use of rock armour (large boulders). The impacts of hard engineering are usually positive (for example, protection from flooding) but they might also be negative. For example, sea walls can make access to the beach more difficult and rock armour could be perceived as ugly, or a potential danger for young children. Groynes prevent longshore drift from transporting sediment along the coast and, in some cases, this has increased the rate of erosion elsewhere. We could investigate hard engineering strategies by:

- taking and then annotating photographs like Figure 10;
- conducting bipolar surveys like Figure 11;
- asking local people about their attitude to coastal management in a questionnaire.

Study Figure 10. The annotations describe how each strategy protects the low-lying land behind. Notice how the annotations are numbered so that they tell a story.

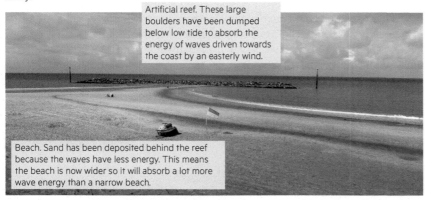

Artificial reef. These large boulders have been dumped below low tide to absorb the energy of waves driven towards the coast by an easterly wind.

Beach. Sand has been deposited behind the reef because the waves have less energy. This means the beach is now wider so it will absorb a lot more wave energy than a narrow beach.

Figure 10 Use annotations to analyse how the management strategy works. Hard engineering at Sea Palling.

Positive evaluation	+2	+1	0	-1	-2	Negative evaluation
Good access to beach						Poor access to beach
Likely to prevent floods						Unlikely to prevent floods
Protects habitats						Disturbs habitats

Figure 11 A bipolar survey designed to assess hard engineering strategies.

Practice questions

1 **Study Figure 8. Explain one conclusion that could be reached about flood risk in this location. Use evidence in the photograph.** **[2]**

2 **Study Figure 11.**
  2.1 Suggest another pair of evaluation statements that could be added to Figure 11. **[2]**
  2.2 Explain why the use of Figure 11 by several different groups of students could give unreliable data. **[2]**

Figure 12 EQI scores for two coastal locations.

> **Exam advice**
> A good evaluation is balanced. Make sure you mention strengths as well as weaknesses.

3 **A student used Figure 9 to collect EQI scores in two coastal locations. One location was a ferry port. The other was a small coastal village. The student drew Figure 12 with the results.**
  3.1 Explain two conclusions that can be reached from this evidence. **[4]**
  3.2 Evaluate the decision to weight the EQI in this way. **[4]**

Investigating sand dunes

While some coastlines are protected using hard engineering, others are managed using more natural methods known as **soft engineering**. These include re-profiling and beach nourishment (adding sand or shingle) as well as the management of sand dunes. Sand dunes are formed at the top of some beaches by the deposition of sand by the wind. Sand dunes absorb wave energy during a storm and protect the land behind from flooding.

Embryo dunes A few specialised plants that are tolerant of salt spray live here, like this sea rocket. They take nutrients from decomposing seaweed washed up in the strand line near the top of the beach.

Mobile dunes Marram grass grows here – it has large fibrous roots that hold the sand together. The tall leaves stick up into the air and slow the wind speed so that sand carried in the wind is deposited. Wind easily erodes sand where there are no plants.

Fixed dunes This is the oldest part of the dunes. Wind speeds are lower here so erosion is less likely. There are more nutrients in the soil because plants have been dropping leaf litter here for longer than elsewhere in the dunes. Consequently, the fixed dunes have a wide variety of flowering plants, shorter grasses, and shrubs like this bramble.

Figure 13 A cross section through a sand dune ecosystem.

Management

Sand dunes are vulnerable to erosion so they need management to keep their ecosystem healthy. Where people trample through the dunes the marram dies and the sand is eroded by the wind. If the sand dunes are badly damaged they are at risk of erosion during storms. Management techniques include:

■ fencing off areas that have been eroded to prevent further damage and replanting with marram;

■ the creation of boardwalks to control the movement of people through the dunes;

■ information boards and signage to educate visitors.

Practice questions

1 Study Figure 13. Students recorded plant types along the cross section. They used stratified sampling to record wind speed on each ridge and in the troughs between each ridge.

1.1 Identify one enquiry question or hypothesis that could be investigated using fieldwork in this environment. [1]

1.2 Explain two reasons why stratified sampling was a suitable strategy. [4]

2 The students used their data on plant types to draw Figure 14.

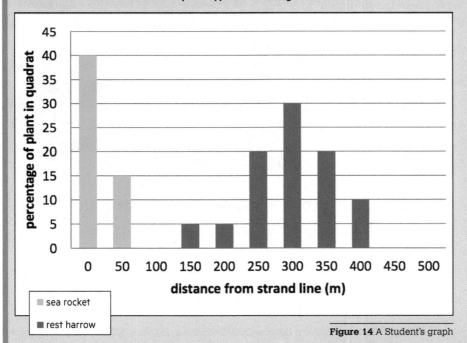

Figure 14 A Student's graph

2.1 Describe the pattern that can be seen in Figure 14. [2]

2.2 A student had the following hypothesis:

'Sea rocket only grows in embryo dunes.'

To what extent does the evidence in Figure 14 prove this hypothesis to be true? [4]

3 Justify one data collection technique that could be used to investigate the effectiveness of sand dune management. [4]

Exam advice

Read the command word. Justify means to give reasons for your decision. If you only describe the technique you will get zero marks.

Chapter 8

River investigations

Learning objectives
- How to draw a cross section of a river channel.

Investigating river processes

The processes of erosion, transportation, and deposition all happen in river channels like the one shown in Figure 1. Sediment is transported down the river. Where water has less energy, as in the shallow water at X, sediment is deposited. You can see evidence of this in the photograph – pebbles have been deposited in a river beach, also known as a **point bar** or **slip-off slope**. Erosion also occurs in meandering river channels. Erosion tends to occur on the outside bend of the meander where water flows with greater energy - forming a river cliff like the one at Y in Figure 1.

Figure 1 A meandering river channel.

We could investigate the processes in this river channel by:
- measuring the depth and width of the river channel and drawing a cross section;
- measuring the velocity of the water and calculating discharge (see pages 84-85);
- analysing the size of pebbles on the river's bed and point bar to find evidence of sorting;
- taking photos or making field sketches and annotating the main features (see pages 32-34).

Creating a cross section of a river channel

To create a cross section of the river channel you will need to follow these steps.

Step One Measure the width of the river channel. Divide this by 10 to create 10 evenly spaced sample points. In Figure 2 the channel is 3m across, so the samples are 30cm apart.

Step Two Stretch a line tightly across the river. Make sure it is level.

Step Three Measure downwards, from the line to the ground, at each sample point. In Figure 2, measurements were made every 30cm on each side of the river as well as into the river channel. Record the distance from the line to the surface of the water.

Figure 2 How to take data readings to create a cross section across a river channel. Shropshire Hills AONB.

Dos and don'ts of river cross sections

Do:	Don't:
Include some of the river bank on either side so that you can draw the river's banks on your cross section. Then you can estimate how much water would be in the river channel when river levels rise.	Let the line droop in the middle. If it does, the measurements for the middle of the channel will be too small.

Sampling pebble size

Point bars (slip-off slopes) are common features in meandering river channels. They form where water flows more slowly on the inside bend of the meander. Large pebbles can be transported along the river's bed in the deepest part of the channel where the river has plenty of energy. Higher up the point bar the water flows slowly so pebbles are deposited. To investigate whether pebble sizes vary up and down a point bar, use a hypothesis such as:

'Pebble sizes are smaller at the top of the point bar than in the deepest part of the river channel.'

To investigate this hypothesis you would need to follow these steps.

Step One Set up a transect at right angles to the river and up the point bar.

Step Two Decide on a sampling strategy. For example, you could collect data from 10 equally spaced sites along the transect as in Figure 3. Measuring the b-axis is the quickest way to do this (see Figure 2 on page 75).

Step Three Select and measure 25 pebbles from each sample site.

Step Four Draw a histogram (see page 48) to analyse your results.

Figure 3 Regular sampling of pebbles from the deepest part of the river channel to the top of the point bar.

Practice questions

1 **Study Figure 1.**

   1.1 Identify **two** potential risks that could occur while doing fieldwork in this environment. [1]

   1.2 For one of these risks, suggest **how** this risk could be reduced. [1]

Investigating river discharge

River discharge is the amount of water flowing down the river channel per second. Discharge is measured in cubic metres per second (cumecs). To investigate discharge you will need to:

■ measure the width and average depth of the river channel. This will allow you to calculate the area of water in the river channel's cross section;

■ measure the velocity of the river's flow.

One way to measure velocity is with a **flow meter**. You can see one being used in Figure 4. You should stand downstream of the flow meter. If you stand upstream your legs will disturb the flow of water and make the results inaccurate. The advantage of a flow meter is that you can use it to record velocities at precise depths in the water channel and also at different points across the width of the channel.

You can also calculate velocity by timing how long it takes for a float to travel downstream. Use something biodegradable like a dog biscuit as the float. You will need two people, a tape, and a stop watch.

Step One Measure a length of 10 metres along the river bank.

Step Two Place the dog biscuit in the water at the start of the 10 metres. Time how long it takes for the float to reach the end of the course.

Step Three Repeat the experiment at least three times. Calculate an average time by adding the results together and dividing by the number of experiments.

Step Four Calculate the velocity by dividing distance by the average time it took for the float to travel downstream. For example, if the average time was 78 seconds then the velocity would be 10 metres divided by 78 seconds, giving a stream velocity of 0.128 metres per second.

Figure 4 Student measuring river flow with a flow meter.

Calculating discharge

River discharge is the volume of water which flows through a river channel in a given amount of time. It is usually measured in cubic metres per second (cumecs). River discharge is calculated by multiplying the river velocity by the cross-sectional area of the channel.

In GCSE Geography, cross-sectional area can be calculated as:

width of the river channel (m) x average mean depth (m) = m^2

river discharge = cross-sectional area (m^2) x velocity (m/s) = m^3/s (cumecs)

Practice questions

1 Study Figures 5, 6, and 7. A student investigated the hypothesis:
'Water flows faster on the outside bend of the meander.'

Figure 5 A student used a float to measure velocity at 5 points across this river channel.

Figure 6 Sketch map of the river in Figure 5 showing the five float positions and the start and end points used to measure the river's flow.

Float	Float time (seconds)			Total (seconds)	Average time (seconds)	Velocity
	First	**Second**	**Third**			
A	54	50	58	162	54	0.19
B	57	61	59	177	59	0.17
C	64	98	66	228		0.13
D	67	68	72	207	69	
E	78	82	89	249	83	0.12

Figure 7 Table of river velocity readings taken at the river shown in Figure 5

1.1 Explain one way that this sampling method made the data more reliable. [2]

1.2 Identify one anomaly in this data. [1]

1.3 Calculate the average time for float C. Show your working. [2]

1.4 Calculate the velocity for float D. Show your working. [2]

1.5 What conclusion can you reach from studying the evidence in Figure 6 and Figure 7? [4]

Exam advice

A good conclusion will refer back to the original aim or hypothesis. It makes direct use of evidence.

Learning objectives

- How to investigate the impact of trampling.

Investigating impacts of tourism

The rugged mountains and hills of upland Britain attract a lot of visitors. Like bees around a pot of honey, these **honeypot sites** attract a lot of visitors. Tourism creates important benefits for the economy and people of upland Britain. It helps to sustain jobs in hotels, guest houses, pubs, and restaurants. The rise in adventure tourism, such as mountain biking, zip wires, and climbing, creates jobs for specialist clothing shops, instructors, guides, and cycle hire shops. As well as these positive contributions tourism also has negative impacts on the landscape, on wildlife, and on rural communities. These can include:

- footpath erosion and trampling of vegetation;
- litter and noise nuisance;
- issues to do with traffic congestion in narrow country roads and parking in gateways.

We could investigate the impacts of tourism at this honeypot site by:

- investigating footpath erosion by measuring cross sections of the path. We could do this at different distances from the car park to test the theory that most environmental impacts occur close to where visitors park their cars;
- using quadrats to investigate whether some plants are more vulnerable to trampling than others;
- using questionnaires to find out where visitors have come from, what they do, and how they spend their money in the local area.

Figure 1 Footpath erosion in Dovedale, in the Peak District National Park.

How to investigate soil erosion

Trampling kills plants leaving the soil exposed so it is easily eroded by rainwater and by hikers' boots. We can record the amount of footpath erosion by stretching a line across the path and measuring down to the ground. The method is similar to drawing a river's cross section (page 82-83) and can be seen in Figure 2.

Figure 2 How to take data readings to create a cross section across an eroded footpath. Shropshire Hills AONB.

Distance along transect (cm)	0	100	200	300	400	500	600	700	800	900
Distance from line to ground (cm)	25	27	29	45	52	47	42	40	26	24

Figure 3 Data readings

Belt transects

Some plant types are hardier than others. They survive trampling whereas other plants are killed. We could investigate this by using quadrats to sample vegetation across the path in a **belt transect**.

Step One Take control readings away from the path to discover which plants grow in an area unaffected by trampling.

Step Two Sample vegetation in a line across the path using a belt transect as shown in Figure 4.

Placing the quadrats end-to-end makes a continuous belt transect. No variations in the vegetation are missed using this technique but it is time-consuming. Placing the quadrats at regular intervals makes an interrupted belt transect. This is a quicker technique to use over a longer distance but small variations in vegetation can be missed.

Figure 4 Continuous belt transect (A) and interrupted belt transect (B)

Practice questions

1 **Study Figure 1.**
  1.1 Identify **one** hypothesis or enquiry question that could be investigated here. [1]
  1.2 Identify **two** potential risks in this fieldwork location. [2]
  1.3 Suggest how **one** of these risks could be reduced. [2]
  1.3 Evaluate the use of an interrupted belt transect to investigate the footpath seen in Figure 1. [4]
2 **A student investigated trampling at the location shown in Figure 2.**
  2.1 Explain why it is important that the line shown in Figure 2 must be tight and level. [2]

Exam advice

The command word *'Identify'* means you need to make a simple statement. Don't waste time by going into a lot of detail.

Learning objectives
- How to use a conflict matrix.
- Assessing the effect of management.

Investigating management of tourism

Tourism needs to be managed carefully so that the natural beauty of the landscape and its wildlife, culture, and heritage are conserved. Each of the UK's National Parks and Areas of Outstanding Natural Beauty (AONBs) work closely with local councils, landowners, and voluntary organisations to ensure that tourism is managed and its negative impacts are reduced.

Figure 5 Signage at the entrance to Dovedale, a honeypot in the Peak District National Park.

Figure 6 Limestone steps have been created in this part of Dovedale to reduce further erosion. They blend into the landscape because they are made of local stone.

We could investigate the management of tourism by:
- comparing the amount of footpath erosion at sites where there is no management (as in Figure 1 on page 86) and sites that are managed (as in Figure 6);
- using bipolar surveys or questionnaires to find out what visitors think of signage (Figure 5), or facilities such as car parks and public toilets.

Practice questions

1 A student used Figure 7 to investigate the management of tourism in Dovedale.

Figure 7 A student's data collection sheet.

1. How far have you walked today? Tick one box.
Up to 100m ☐
100-500m ☐
300-1000m ☐
Over 1000m ☐
2. Please put a tick to show what you think about how Dovedale is managed.

The site is clean and footpaths well managed					The site is dirty and footpaths badly managed
Signs are helpful					Signs are unhelpful

1.1 Identify two weaknesses in Figure 7 that would make this survey unreliable. [2]

1.2 Suggest how one of these questions could be adapted to improve its reliability. [2]

Using a conflict matrix

A **conflict matrix**, like Figure 8, is a simple way to record potential conflicts between different recreational uses. For example, in areas where there is livestock, dogs should be kept on a lead to avoid conflict with farmers. Some activities, such as mountain biking, could be perceived as a hazard by other users of the space.

Step One Identify the main users in your fieldwork area and create a conflict matrix like Figure 8.

Step Two Collect evidence of any conflict. You could use questionnaires or Likert Surveys to identify the conflicts.

Step Three Record your findings in the conflict matrix using the traffic light key.

	Walking	Dog walking	Mountain biking	Bird watching	Shooting	Sheep farming
Walking	▨					
Dog walking		▨				
Mountain biking			▨			
Bird watching				▨		
Shooting					▨	
Sheep farming						▨

Figure 8 A simple conflict matrix.

Key

▨ Activities are compatible – no conflict

▨ Some potential conflict between uses

▨ Conflict needs management

Practice questions

2 A student collected data on the width of footpaths. Their aim was to investigate whether the width of the footpath depended on distance from the visitor car park. The results are shown in Figure 9.

Figure 9 Student's scatter graph.

2.1 Identify the type of sampling used to collect the data that was used to draw Figure 9. [2]

2.2 Describe the relationship shown in Figure 9. [2]

2.3 Identify one anomaly in the data. [1]

2.4 What conclusion can you reach about the number of tourists who walk over 400m from the car park? Use evidence from Figure 9. [4]

PART 03

Chapter 10

Urban investigations

Learning objectives
- How to collect qualitative data about sustainable urban living.

Investigating sustainable urban living

Poor housing, a lack of green space, traffic congestion, pollution and crime are problems in some UK towns and cities. To make urban areas better places for residents (now and in the future) planners need to make the urban environment more sustainable.

Sustainable urban living means that people have access to local services that they need and that they have a way of life that will last a long time. Residents are well connected by a variety of transport links including buses, safe cycle routes, and pedestrian routes.

Figure 1 Egan's Wheel describes eight key features of sustainable living.

Strong communities – are active, inclusive and safe

Well-designed homes – with green outdoor spaces

Well-served – a full range of public, private and voluntary sector services

Sensitive to the environment – conserving habitats and wildlife

Strong economy – with different types of work available

Governance – so everyone feels that comunities are well-run and led

Transport – so people are well-connected to jobs and services

Fair for everyone – now and in the future

Figure 2 This pedestrian area of Derby is designed with good lighting and strong materials that cannot be easily vandalised. CCTV cameras help to reduce crime and make local residents feel safer.

We can investigate sustainable urban living by assessing some of the key features shown in Figure 1. For example, by:

- **surveying the neighbourhood** - plotting the location of security features on a base map. You could plot the location of CCTV cameras, neighbourhood watch signs, and anti-climb paint;
- **using an Environmental Quality Index (EQI) Survey** to assess the quality of green spaces, transport links, and access to services;
- **interviewing local residents or business people** about features that should strengthen community spirit. How do people perceive the value of community centres, youth clubs, or support groups?

Using Environmental Quality Indices (EQI) to assess sustainability

We can investigate sustainability using EQIs (see pages 28-29) to assess key features of the urban environment.

Step One Select two features from Egan's wheel. Design an EQI like Figure 3.

Step Two Do a pilot survey using your EQI to make sure that it is possible for different students to apply the criteria in a consistent and reliable way. If not, re-write the criteria.

Step Three Design a sampling strategy that will allow you to spot any spatial variations in sustainability across the town/city. You will probably want to use a base map with grid lines (see page 16-17). This is **systematic sampling**.

Step Four Make sure that everyone agrees on how to apply your EQI criteria so that the results are reliable. Decide who is going to each sample point and then collect your data.

Figure 3 You can use an EQI to assess the sustainability of a neighbourhood.

Feature	Criteria				
	5	4	3	2	1
Sensitive to the environment	A wide range of different habitats are available to the public.	Private gardens and communal areas have trees/shrubs as well as grass.	Private gardens have trees/shrubs but communal areas are grass.	Some areas of grass, e.g. lawns, verges, or sports fields.	No green spaces.
	5	4	3	2	1
Well served	A wide range of groups are actively involved in providing local community projects.	A wide range of services are available for different community groups.	Services are available for some different groups in the community.	Some services for local residents.	Very few services for any local residents.

Practice questions

1 **A student investigated sustainable urban living in the area shown in Figure 2.**
   1.1 Suggest one hypothesis or enquiry question that could be investigated here. [1]
2 **The student designed an EQI to assess sustainable features of the city centre. Their EQI is shown in Figure 4.**
   2.1 Identify **two** possible problems with the student's EQI in Figure 4. [2]
   2.2 Suggest **one** way that this EQI could be improved. [2]
   2.3 Suggest **one** way that data on location of CCTV could be presented. Justify your choice. [4]

Feature	Criteria				
	5	4	3	2	1
Strong communities	Frequent CCTV cameras and a wide range of other crime prevention strategies are used.	Some CCTV cameras and at least one other type of deterrent e.g. neighbourhood watch signs.	A lot of graffiti and some vandalism.	Good street lighting.	No evidence of any crime prevention strategies.
	5	4	3	2	1
Transport	Frequent bus services with bus lanes. Cycle lanes are well used.	Lots of bus lanes and bus stops.	Some bus services and some cycle lanes.	Infrequent bus services. No cycle lanes	No public transport. No cycle lanes

Figure 4 The student's EQI.

Choropleth maps

A **choropleth** is a type of map where darker colours (or darker shading) are used to represent higher data values. To draw a **dot map** (see page 56) you need to know the exact location of each item of data. For example, you could use a dot map to show the location of CCTV cameras, or speed bumps. A choropleth represents data from geographical areas rather than specific points so they are ideal if you planned a systematic survey of a town as we described on pages 16-17.

Step One Make a simple base map using the grid lines of your OS map.

Step Two Decide how many colours or shades you are going to use. One for each EQI score would be sensible – so five colours.

Step Three Create a key. Use dark colours for the highest values and lighter colours for lower values.

Step Four Colour each area on the map. Do this by checking the data value for each area and comparing it to the key.

Step Five Give your map a title.

Strengths and limitations of choropleth maps	
Strengths	**Some limitations**
• The darker colours clearly show where data values are higher. • You don't need to know pin-point locations for your data.	• Choosing the right number of colours is important – too many or too few colours will make it difficult to see a pattern.

Practice questions

Figure 5 A student's choropleth of Shrewsbury showing results from an EQI to survey access to services.

Key
- 5 excellent access to services
- 4
- 3
- 2
- 1 poor access to services

1 **A large group of students used an EQI to investigate access to services in Shrewsbury. They worked in teams to collect data from the grid squares shown in Figure 5 on page 16. Each team surveyed four grid squares. They presented their data in Figure 5 on page 92.**
   1.1 Describe the pattern shown in Figure 5. [2]
   1.2 Identify one anomaly in the data. [1]
   1.3 Explain why the sampling method used may have led to unreliable results. [2]

Exam advice
Reliability depends on data being collected by different groups in exactly the same way.

Investigating urban transport

Think about the impacts of the busy road shown in Figure 6. On the one hand, local people are well connected to other places, especially if the road has a bus route. On the other hand, it has negative impacts. Traffic noise may disturb local residents. Traffic jams delay the delivery of goods to local businesses. Pollution can cause health issues. The road may be dangerous to cross. Long commutes, traffic congestion, and pollution are all indicators of unsustainable urban living.

Figure 6 Traffic on a busy road in Birmingham.

We could investigate the impacts of traffic congestion by:
- **taking noise readings** – perhaps using an app on your smart phone. How quickly do noise levels decrease as you move away from the road? Do noise levels vary throughout the day?
- **measure the amount of dust in the atmosphere** - by sticking double-sided tape to buildings to collect dirt and dust on the open sticky side. Is there more dust close to the road?
- **collecting secondary data on house prices**. Do busy roads have a negative impact on house prices?

Practice questions

2 **A student wanted to investigate the effect of busy roads on house prices.**

2.1 Identify one possible risk of fieldwork in the location shown in Figure 6. [1]

2.2 Explain how this risk could be managed. [2]

2.3 Explain why the students need to take several noise meter readings in this location. [2]

2.4 Suggest a sampling strategy to investigate whether house prices are affected by distance from the road. [4]

2.5 Identify two problems with the bipolar survey shown in Figure 7. [2]

Positive	+2	+1	0	-1	-2	Negative
Safe places to cross						No safe place to cross
Not many lorries						Lots of heavy vehicles
Traffic calming						No speed bumps
Noisy						Quiet

Figure 7 A student's bipolar survey.

Part 3 Fieldwork in human environments

93

Investigating urban regeneration

The UK's towns and cities are constantly changing in a process known as **urban regeneration**. As older buildings become derelict they are demolished creating **brownfield sites** that are ready for redevelopment. This is an opportunity for planners to create an attractive urban environment and encourage investment by businesses. Carefully planned regeneration may solve problems such as dereliction and traffic congestion. Ugly buildings can be replaced with cutting-edge modern designs. Traffic systems can be redesigned to make streets safer for pedestrians and cyclists.

Figure 8 The library in Centenary Square, Birmingham. Opened in 2013, this was a flagship building in the regeneration of Centenary Square.

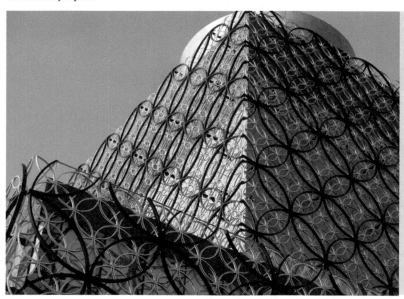

We can use fieldwork to investigate how regeneration has affected the urban landscape by:
- **measuring footfall** (the movement of pedestrians) to see whether areas that have been regenerated have more pedestrians than other parts of the town/city;
- **using EQI surveys** to assess whether regeneration has made the area more sustainable than other parts of the town/city.

Footfall (a pedestrian count) in a public open space like a park or pedestrian area can be tricky to measure because of the number of people and the complexity of their movement. For example, they may change direction, or walk in groups with few gaps between them. One strategy to improve the accuracy of the count is for three people to count at the same location for five minutes. Then, calculate the average (see pages 40-41).

Figure 9 A student's questionnaire.

1 Tick the boxes that best describe your opinions about the regeneration of Centenary Square and Paradise Circus.

	Strongly agree	Agree	Neutral	Disagree	Strongly disagree
The new library is more attractive than the 1970s building it replaced.					
Centenary Square is a nice place to spend some time.					

2 In your opinion, is Centenary Square a safe place for pedestrians and is the sign posting to other parts of the city clear?

3 What do you think are the main benefits of urban regeneration in Birmingham?

Investigating opinions

Regeneration can be used to change people's perceptions of an older urban area – making it seem more modern, friendly, and business-like. We can use fieldwork to investigate whether different groups of people have differing opinions about regeneration. To do this follow these steps.

Step One Decide on your enquiry question. For example, do younger or older people prefer modern architecture?

Step Two Design a questionnaire, bipolar survey, or Likert Survey.

Step Three Design a data recording sheet. Figure 10 has been designed to use with the bipolar survey in Figure 11.

Step Four Identify the mode in the results. In Figure 10, the mode for the question about architecture is +3.

Step Five You could present the data in a located bar chart, like Figure 12.

Positive	+3	+2	+1	0	-1	-2	-3	Negative
Interesting architecture								Boring architecture
Safe and easy for pedestrians								Dangerous and difficult for pedestrians

Tally for Centenary Square		
Bipolar score	**architecture**	**pedestrians**
+3	⊬⊬ |||		
+2	⊬⊬	
+1	||	|||
0	||	⊬⊬
-1	|||	||
-2		⊬⊬ ||
-3		||

Figure 10 A tally chart for a bipolar count.

Figure 11 A student's bipolar survey.

Figure 12 A student's located bar map of a transect through Birmingham.

Practice questions

1 **A student investigated regeneration on a transect through Birmingham.**
  1.1 Explain two ways that the questionnaire shown in Figure 9 could be adapted to make it more reliable. [4]
  1.2 Suggest one way that the bipolar survey shown in Figure 10 could be adapted to make it more reliable. [1]

Exam advice

Think about the common errors made in questionnaires and how these can be corrected.

Investigating green spaces in the urban environment

The UK's towns and cities provide many opportunities for recreation and leisure. Green spaces provide places for relaxation, sport, dog walking, and exercise, for example, jogging. Sometimes recreation is organised, such as a park run. Green spaces also provide safe routes for pedestrians and cyclists where they are separated from vehicles. Footpaths and cycle paths that follow canals or rivers, like the one in Figure 13, allow commuters to travel through the city quickly and safely. By creating safe pedestrian and cycling routes, planners can help to reduce traffic congestion and these routes can become part of an **integrated transport** system if they are linked to bus routes or train stations.

Environmental benefits

Green spaces provide habitat for urban wildlife such as butterflies, moths, bats, garden birds, and mammals such as foxes. Trees help to reduce noise and traffic pollution. Vegetation helps to reduce the risk of flooding by intercepting water and reducing the time it takes for heavy rainfall to reach urban rivers. Planners now encourage the creation of **Pocket Parks** – tiny green spaces that benefit the local community and the environment.

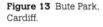

Figure 13 Bute Park, Cardiff.

We could investigate the use of this green space by:

- **observing how people use the space:** How do people in different groups (such as teenagers, adults, families) use the space? Do these different groups use the space for different amounts of time?
- **photographing any evidence that the park is being managed**, such as signs about cycling, ball games, or litter;
- **interviewing people who use the park (or pocket park)** about the health or well-being benefits;
- **searching social media** to find people's views about the use of the park, such as attendance at a park run event.

Practice questions

Figure 14 River Taff in Cardiff creates a green corridor through the city. Pedestrians and cyclists commute along this corridor.

Figure 15 Student's flow line maps of pedestrian flows.

1 **A group of students counted pedestrians walking through green areas of Cardiff. They split into 7 different groups to collect data at each of the locations shown in Figure 15.**

   1.1 Identify **one** possible risk in the location shown in Figure 14.   [1]

   1.2 Identify **two** different reasons that their pedestrian counts may have been unreliable.   [2]

   1.3 Suggest **one** way of improving the reliability of their data.   [2]

   1.4 Explain **one** conclusion that can be drawn from Figure 15.   [4]

Exam advice

In 1.4 the examiner will expect you to try to give reasons for any patterns you can see. Use evidence from the maps.

Learning objectives

- How to investigate opinions about the impact of rural tourism.

Investigating rural tourism

In the past, the rural economy relied on farming. Nowadays people living in the countryside make a living from a variety of part-time and full-time jobs. This is known as **rural diversification**. Many of the new jobs are in the leisure sector with jobs created in activities related to hospitality, such as camping, glamping, and catering; and in outdoor activities, such as mountain biking, horse riding, or kayaking.

Tourists are attracted to cultural events such as music and arts festivals in rural areas. These festivals have impacts on the environment and local economy. Positive impacts can be created when visitors spend money in local shops, cafes, pubs, or hotels. However, events and festivals can also create negative impacts such as noise, traffic congestion, parking issues, or anti-social behaviour. You could use a fieldwork enquiry to evaluate whether the positive impacts of tourism outweigh any negative impacts. It may be that some groups of people in the local area are more positive about the impacts of tourism than others. If so, you could use your fieldwork to try to find out why.

Figure 1 A weekend festival in Bishop's Castle, Shropshire. The high street was closed for the weekend to allow the procession to take place.

We could investigate the impacts of a rural festival such as this by:

- comparing traffic congestion, parking issues, and flows of pedestrians on the day of the event with a day when the event is not taking place;
- using a questionnaire to ask local people and visitors about the impacts of the event. Does one group of people have a more positive view of the event than the other group?

Practice questions

1 A student investigated the impact of the temporary closure of the high street in a rural town during a festival as shown in Figure 1. They set the following hypothesis and created a sampling strategy, as in Figure 2.

'Visitors are generally in favour of the road closure but local people think it is a nuisance.'

Figure 2 Sampling strategy

	Total number	Number of people in the sample
Local people (who live in the town)	2,500	10
Visitors to the event	1,250	50

1.1 Identify **one** limitation in this sampling strategy. [1]

1.2 If the student used a stratified sampling technique and asked 30 local people, how many visitors should he ask? Show your workings. [2]

1.3 Give **one** reason why a stratified sample would have given more reliable results than that used by the student. [2]

2 The results of the Likert Survey are shown in Figure 3. The student presented these results in the graph shown in Figure 4.

Figure 3 The student's results.

'The closure of the main street to traffic was a good thing'	Number of responses from:	
	Local people	Visitors
Strongly agree	0	10
Agree	1	30
Neutral	1	7
Disagree	5	2
Strongly disagree	3	1

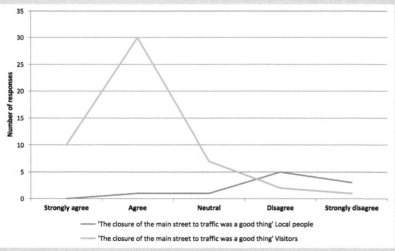

Figure 4 The student's graph.

2.1 Evaluate the way the results are presented in Figure 4. [4]

2.2 Use the evidence in Figure 2 to reach a conclusion about whether *'The closure of the main street to traffic was a good thing'*. [2]

2.3 Suggest two reasons why some locals may have disagreed with the statement. Use evidence from Figure 1. [4]

Exam advice

To evaluate the graph you need to think about what is good and what is bad about it. Think about the type of data – is a line graph suitable?

Investigating rural deprivation

Many rural areas of the UK face a number of social and economic issues. If you live in the countryside it can be a long journey to the nearest shop, school, post office, theatre, or sports centre. Just getting to the nearest shop can be tricky because there aren't many buses. Some rural areas face challenging **socio-economic** issues too such as:

■ an ageing population with a shortage of facilities for elderly residents;
■ a lack of well-paid, full-time work.

Figure 5 The closure of rural shops and services is a big issue in many rural communities. Bishop's Castle, Shropshire.

We can investigate issues of rural deprivation by:

■ asking local residents about which services they use and how far they have to travel to use them;
■ using Likert surveys to assess how locals feel about the closure of rural services;
■ using secondary data from the census or a GIS site to collect evidence of rural deprivation.

Coastal rural communities

Some smaller seaside towns have particular problems with low incomes. Traditional fishing jobs have been lost. Jobs in tourism have declined as holidays abroad have become cheaper. Study Figure 6. Notice the cluster of orange and red areas close to the seaside town of Skegness and in rural Lincolnshire which indicate a standard of living that is below UK average.

Figure 6 Choropleth showing multiple deprivation. Areas coloured blue/green have an above average standard of living. Areas coloured orange/red have a below average standard of living – these are areas suffering deprivation.

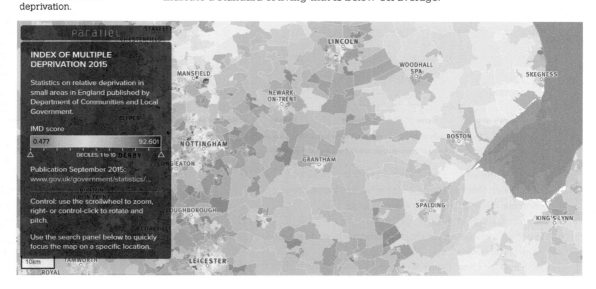

INDEX OF MULTIPLE DEPRIVATION 2015

Statistics on relative deprivation in small areas in England published by Department of Communities and Local Government.

IMD score

0.477 — 92.601

DECILES: 1 to 10

Publication September 2015:
www.gov.uk/government/statistics/...

Control: use the scrollwheel to zoom, right- or control-click to rotate and pitch.

Use the search panel below to quickly focus the map on a specific location.

10km

Secondary evidence of rural deprivation

It can be difficult to collect primary data about inequality or deprivation. Most people don't like talking about personal details so you should avoid questions about jobs, income, and health. Instead, we can use secondary data sources such as the census or GIS maps to collect social and economic data about the rural area. We can find data on house prices, crime, job types, qualifications and the age structure of the rural population. Examples can be seen in Figures 6 and 7.

GIS maps can be used to help design data sampling. For example, we can use maps like Figure 6 to plan a route for a transect through a rural area. You could use stratified sampling – visiting one place of each colour on the map – and carrying out EQI surveys at each sample site.

Practice questions

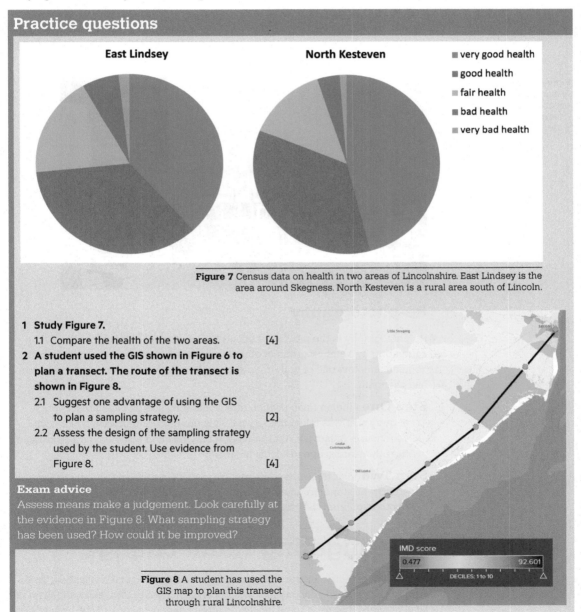

East Lindsey   **North Kesteven**

- very good health
- good health
- fair health
- bad health
- very bad health

Figure 7 Census data on health in two areas of Lincolnshire. East Lindsey is the area around Skegness. North Kesteven is a rural area south of Lincoln.

1 **Study Figure 7.**
  1.1 Compare the health of the two areas. [4]
2 **A student used the GIS shown in Figure 6 to plan a transect. The route of the transect is shown in Figure 8.**
  2.1 Suggest one advantage of using the GIS to plan a sampling strategy. [2]
  2.2 Assess the design of the sampling strategy used by the student. Use evidence from Figure 8. [4]

Exam advice
Assess means make a judgement. Look carefully at the evidence in Figure 8. What sampling strategy has been used? How could it be improved?

Figure 8 A student has used the GIS map to plan this transect through rural Lincolnshire.

Learning objectives
■ How to assess the impact of economic decline on the urban landscape.

Investigating evidence of deindustrialisation

In the 1960s there were plenty of Victorian factories, docks, warehouses, and chimneys in use. The process of **deindustrialisation** had a big impact on the urban environment. As industries like coal mining and steel making declined, these buildings and the surrounding sites became derelict and vandalised. Some sites were badly affected by pollution and were dangerous places.

Many old industrial sites have been carefully redeveloped to create new space for housing, shops, roads, or new offices and factories. Other sites have been cleaned and made safe so that important historic buildings can be conserved for the future. Canals, for example, were once used for transporting goods such as coal. Now they are used for recreation and the warehouses that once overlooked them have been converted to luxury flats, bars, or offices. We can use fieldwork to investigate how the changing economy has affected the urban landscape.

Figure 9 Bars and restaurants have replaced warehouses on Birmingham's canal network.

Re-photography

Re-photography is the process of taking a photograph now (primary data) and comparing it to a photograph or other image taken in the past (secondary data). You can annotate one or both images to analyse the ways in which the landscape has changed.

Step One Find an image which represents the location of your fieldwork enquiry that was taken in the past. This might be a photograph of a dock, warehouse, or factory. Alternatively, it may be an image such as a painting of the urban landscape in a local museum.

Step Two Visit the same place and try to work out where the camera (or artist) was standing when the original photograph was taken. Take a new photograph from the same position.

Investigating retail change

Some town and city centres face serious economic and social challenges. Vacant (empty) shops, traffic congestion, lack of parking, litter, graffiti, and vandalism are all challenges that need to be tackled to attract shoppers back to the high street.

The high proportion of vacant shops, betting shops, charity shops, and 'pound' shops in some high streets creates a particular economic challenge. More vacant shops mean fewer shoppers. Unless something can be done to make the high street more attractive, even more shops may close. Burslem, Stoke-on-Trent, seen in Figure 10, has one of the highest proportions of vacant shops in the UK.

We can use fieldwork to investigate the challenges facing the high street by:
- **classifying and mapping shop types**, including vacant shops;
- **using an EQI to assess environmental challenges** such as graffiti, vandalism, traffic, or parking issues (see pages 28-29);
- **using a questionnaire to find out whether shoppers are satisfied** with the quality of pavements, street furniture, or signage that directs them around the town centre (see pages 26-27).

Figure 10 Google Street View of Burslem in Stoke. The sliding bar shows that 5 sets of images are available, starting in 2011 and ending in 2017.

Using Google Street View

Google Street View can be used to collect secondary data about land use in the recent past. The date that the photographs were taken is in the top left of the screen. Most streets have been photographed 5 or 6 times by Google since about 2009. By comparing this secondary data to the primary data you collect during your fieldtrip, you can see how land uses have changed. In particular, you can identify shops that have closed or changed hands since the 'Street View' images were last taken. The change in the percentage of two types of shops is particularly interesting:
- empty (or vacant) shops – because an increase in vacant shops may indicate that fewer shoppers are using the town;
- locally owned (or independent shops) - because a decline in independent shops may indicate that the town is losing some of its identity and becoming more of a clone town.

Practice questions

1 **Study Figure 10.**
   1.1 Assess the use of photographs as secondary data in geography fieldwork. [4]

Learning objectives
■ How to assess how well your local town centre is connected to global and local businesses.

Investigating global and local economic links

The UK is part of a global network that is linked through trade, business, and the media. The UK's town centres show clear evidence of these economic links with the rest of the world. Famous high street names such as Aldi, Lidl, Topshop, Body Shop, Starbucks, Costa, Virgin Megastore, and HSBC are all owned by big **multinational companies**. Many other high street shops are chain stores - part of a national network of stores under the same ownership. **Chain stores** make savings by importing goods from all over the world to meet our demand for cheap clothes, food or electronic goods.

Figure 11 Mr Pugh. An independent butcher in Bishop's Castle, Shropshire.

https://www.gov.uk/correct-your-business-rates
This online tool allows you to find the rateable value of shops in your high street.

We can use fieldwork to investigate the global economic links of the high street by:

■ **plotting retail land uses** and identifying multinationals, chain stores, and locally owned independent shops;

■ **measuring footfall** (pedestrian flows) in different town centre locations to see whether there is any connection between footfall and rateable value.

Investigating footfall and shop type

Retailers want their shops to be in locations that have high **footfall** – this simply means places where there are large numbers of pedestrians. These locations are highly desirable. Consequently, shop owners tend to pay a higher rate of tax (known as the rateable value) for these shops. This relationship may explain why many small, locally owned businesses can no longer afford to locate in the busiest streets of our town centres. Charity shops pay lower business rates so can operate in areas which independent shops can no longer afford.

Local links

Other shops are independents. These shops are owned by local business people. Many stock local produce, like the butcher shown in Figure 11. Mr Pugh buys all of his meat from farms less than 10km from his shop and it is slaughtered locally too. Some consumers prefer to buy this kind of produce – they want to support local businesses and they want their shopping to have a lower impact on the environment because of the lower **food miles**. This is a measure of the distance your weekly shopping has travelled before it arrives on your plate.

Figure 12 Costa is a British multinational company. It is the second largest coffee chain in the world after Starbucks – which is a US multinational company.

Figure 13 A student's map of Shrewsbury

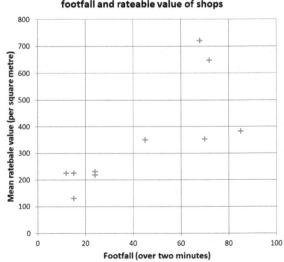

Figure 14 A student's scatter graph representing data collected in Shrewsbury.

1 **Study Figures 13 and 14.**

1.1 State which shopping area has over 75% chain stores. [1]

1.2 Describe the location of the shopping area that has most independent shops. [2]

1.3 Describe the correlation shown in Figure 14. [2]

1.4 To what extent does the evidence support the conclusion that independent shops are more likely to locate in pedestrian streets where footfall is highest? Use evidence from Figures 13 and 14. [6]

What is assessed in Paper 3?

Learning objectives
- Understanding how Paper 3 is structured and marked.

How is Paper 3 structured?

Your understanding of fieldwork is assessed in Paper 3. Paper 3 is marked out of 76 marks, which includes 6 marks for the accuracy of your spelling, punctuation, and grammar (SPG). You will have one hour and fifteen minutes to do the exam.

The exam paper is divided into two Sections.

Section A - the issue evaluation
- Section A is worth 34 marks plus 3 marks for SPG.
  You will be given a resources booklet 12 weeks before your Paper 3 exam.
- The questions in Section A assess your ability to evaluate a geographical issue that is described in the resources booklet.
- Chapter 13 gives some tips on how to study the resources booklet before the exam. You will be given a new, clean copy of the resources booklet at the start of the exam.

Section B – fieldwork assessment
- Section B is worth 36 marks plus 3 marks for SPG.
- You will be asked questions about both human and physical geography fieldwork enquiries.
- The questions in Section B could be about any of the six stages of the enquiry process.
- To answer some questions you will need to respond to stimulus materials in the exam paper. Other questions will be about your own fieldwork enquiries.
- Chapter 14 gives some ideas about how to revise for Section B and Chapter 15 gives advice about how to answer fieldwork questions.

How is Paper 3 marked?

Figure 1 shows you how Paper 3 will be marked. Over half of the marks are for Assessment Objective 3 (AO3) which assesses your ability to analyse, evaluate, and make decisions. So, it is important to prepare for your exam by thinking critically about the resources booklet and your fieldwork experiences.

What are the assessment objectives?

First, there are no marks for AO1 in Paper 3. AO1 is your ability to remember geographical facts. So, if the resources booklet is about river management there is no point trying to learn specific case studies about river floods, or how a particular river has been managed. Understanding what is involved in river management is useful.

Figure 2 explains what each of the assessment objectives is actually testing. Most of the marks in Paper 3 are for AO3 and AO4, so, to prepare for Paper 3 you need to think critically about information in the resources booklet and what you did in your fieldwork. You also need to practise using a variety of maps, graphs, and numeracy skills.

Figure 1 How Paper 3 is marked.

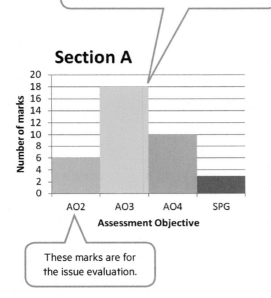

18 marks are for your ability to analyse, evaluate, or justify your decisions. For example, can you decide which strategy might help solve the issue described in the resources booklet?

These marks are for the issue evaluation.

Half of the marks assess your ability to analyse, evaluate, or justify your decision. For example, can you weigh up the strengths and weaknesses of your sampling strategy? Can you evaluate the aim of your fieldwork, or justify the way you decided to represent your data in a graph or map?

These marks are for your fieldwork.

AO2 **6**	AO2 is only assessed in Section A. Examiners will want to see that you **understand** the issues presented in the resources booklet. 6 marks are for showing that understanding.	Use words like *'because'*, *'which means that'*, *'consequently'* and *'so'* to show that you are making connections.
AO3 **42**	A massive 42 marks are for **analysis, evaluation, or decision making**. For example, can you decide which strategy might help solve the issue described in the resources booklet? Can you evaluate the sampling technique you used in your fieldwork enquiry?	Use words like *'strengths'*, *'limitations'*, *'short term'* and *'long term'* to show you can evaluate.
AO4 **22**	A total of 22 marks are for demonstrating your ability to use **geographical skills**. For example, can you read data from a map or graph in the resources booklet, or one you see for the first time in the exam paper?	Use words that describe trends and patterns like *'fluctuating'*, *'rapidly increasing'*, *'doubled'*, or *'clustered'*.

Figure 2 Get to know the assessment objectives.

Chapter 13
Preparing for Section A – Issue Evaluation

Learning objectives
■ How to use the resources booklet to prepare for the exam.
■ Strategies for structuring your longer answers in Section A of the exam.

The Pre-release resources booklet

12 weeks before the exam your school will receive copies of the Pre-release resources booklet. This booklet will contain information about a geographical issue. The issue is something that people have different ideas about. For example, the resources booklet could be about:

■ how to improve quality of life in one of the world's poorer cities;
■ ways to make UK cities more sustainable;
■ the best way to manage a river and prevent it from causing flood damage;
■ whether or not to protect a coastal community from erosion by the sea.

The issue can be from any part of your geography course so the resources booklet could be about one of these issues, or it could be about one of the other topics that are covered in the AQA specification.

Analysing photographs

Photos are important pieces of evidence. A simple way to find meaning in any photo is to follow the steps below and look at the example shown in Figure 1.

Step One Identify the key geographical features of the photo. These are things that you recognise from your geography lessons. They might be landforms. In Figure 1 they are features of a major city in a newly emerging economy (NEE). Write a simple label for each feature.

Step Two Link your labels to the photo with an arrow.

Step Three Now you are going to use what you have learned in geography lessons to think about consequences. Imagine how the features shown in this photo might affect local people, the environment, or jobs and work (the economy).

Step Four For each feature write down at least one consequence. If there's enough space you can do this next to the photo. You could use a different colour for this annotation, as in Figure 1. If not, make a separate list of features and their consequences.

Activities

1 Study Figure 1. Use your understanding of the issues facing cities in a newly emerging economy, like the one shown in the photo, to complete the elaboration for statements 3, 4 and 5.

Homes are built on a very steep hillside …

So they could be at risk of landslides during heavy rainfall.

Homes are small and very close together …

So there is a risk that fire from a cooking stove could quickly spread through the whole neighbourhood.

This building seems to have had extra floors built on top which might indicate that the city has grown rapidly without proper planning control …

So some homes may not have a safe supply of electricity or clean water.

All of these cables may indicate that people are tapping into the electricity supply.

Which would create health and safety risks.

The road is paved but it is steep and narrow …

So this city may have transport issues with congestion in some parts and not enough public transport for residents.

Key

Features in the photograph

Consequences for people, environment or economy

Figure 1 How to analyse a photograph. This photograph shows La Paz, a large city in Bolivia.

Extending your elaboration

The annotations on Figure 1 are useful but they would be even better if these ideas were extended. You can do this by using connectives to link your ideas together. Words like *'so'*, *'because'*, *'therefore'*, *'which means that'*, are very useful to create longer sentences that show you fully understand something. Examiners call this elaboration and it is a good thing! You are likely to get extra marks for good elaboration. Study Figure 2. Read across each row. Notice how connectives have been used to link ideas together to create a chain of reasoning.

Figure 2 Turn simple statements into fully elaborated consequences.

Simple statement	Consequence	Elaboration	Further elaboration
1. Homes on the hillside are small and very close together …	so there is a risk of fire spreading from a cooking stove …	which would spread quickly from house to house.	Furthermore, it could be very difficult to get a fire engine into the narrow streets.
2. Houses seem to be badly built …	as a result of poor planning controls …	so houses built on the steep slope are at risk of collapse during the rainy season …	because they only have shallow foundations.
3. The sprawling shanty town on the hillside …	is a consequence of rural to urban migration …	which occurs because of pull factors…	
4. Narrow streets are a challenge to planners …	because it is difficult to provide efficient public transport …		
5. Waste collection may be a problem …			

So	Consequence	As a result of
Which means that	because	Due to
Therefore	Thus	For this reason

Figure 3 Use connectives to extend explanation.

Evaluating issues in the resources booklet

You will be studying the resources booklet without knowing exactly what questions you will be asked in the exam. However, you know that 18 marks in Section A will target AO3 – so at least one question is likely to ask you to evaluate something. To evaluate means to weigh up the strengths (or advantages) against the weaknesses (or disadvantages). So, you should study the resources booklet carefully and identify any issues that could be evaluated. For example, in geography you can evaluate:

■ one or more strategies, for example, ways of protecting a coastline;
■ a potential solution to a problem, for example, how to conserve an ecosystem;
■ a planning proposal, for example, how a brownfield site could be developed.

Step One Read the resources booklet and identify what could be evaluated.

Step Two Use different coloured highlighter pens to highlight words or phrases. For example, if the booklet contains a passage that describes a strategy to manage the issue:

■ use one colour of pen to highlight any benefits/advantages of the strategy;
■ use a different colour to highlight any negative impacts/disadvantages of the strategy.

Step Three Create a table like Figure 4. Copy the words/phrases you have highlighted in the resources booklet into the correct boxes of your table. This is sometimes called the 'see' technique because you are identifying social, environmental, and economic impacts.

Figure 4 Use a table to evaluate a strategy, solution, or proposal.

	Strengths / Advantages	Weaknesses / Disadvantages
For people/communities (**social**)		
For the **environment**		
For jobs and businesses (**economy**)		

Figure 5 Use connectives to extend evaluation.

In the short term	The most important	The biggest advantage
In the long term	Another benefit	On the other hand
However	Whereas	Furthermore

Practice decision making

As you analyse the information in the resources booklet it is a good idea to look for issues that need a decision. It would be helpful to ask yourself some questions. For example:

■ What is the issue? What decisions are required?
■ What ought to be done to solve this issue?
■ What might the consequences be for different groups of people?
■ What might happen in the short term and in the long term?
■ Who might benefit most?
■ Is my solution sustainable – for people, the economy, and the environment?

There is a simple sequence of events you can go through to help you practice the skills you need for decision making. The first thing to do is to spot any issues that might need a decision. Highlight them in the resources booklet. Figure 6 provides an example.

Floods have caused misery in Galgate, Lancashire, for the second time in two years. Several homes in this small village, close to Lancaster, were flooded after the River Conder burst its banks. 'We were amazed how quickly the water levels rose,' said one resident. 'The river level had been rising all day but we hoped we would be safe. But when the water started to come in to the house it all happened very quickly. Within a few minutes we had 2ft (60cm) of water. The floorboards have lifted and everything on the ground floor is ruined.' The same houses in Galgate were flooded in December 2015 by rainfall from Storm Desmond. Storm Desmond caused severe damage in the nearby city of Lancaster when the River Lune burst its banks. Town centre shops were flooded and some stayed closed for months. An electricity sub-station was damaged so 55,000 homes in Lancaster and Galgate had no power for over two days.

The recent floods were caused by a period of very heavy rainfall over the northern parts of Lancashire. 73.6mm of rain fell at Lancaster University (2km from Galgate) which was the highest amount for 50 years. Low pressure from the Atlantic brought rain and wind to many parts of the UK as the frontal system passed across the country. However, the low pressure lingered over the North West of England, bringing a long period of heavy rain to an area where the ground was already saturated with water. That's why river levels rose so rapidly.

Residents in Galgate are concerned that their village is at risk of further flooding. 'The council van delivered a few sandbags but there weren't enough to go around,' said one resident. 'Nothing seems to have been done since the last flood. All the money seems to be spent in Lancaster.' Some residents blamed the floods on new houses that have been built on the edge of the village. 'The storm drains on the new housing estate fed the rain straight into the river,' complained one. However, a spokesperson for the Environment Agency said that the exceptional rainfall was the actual cause of the flooding rather that the new housing.

Figure 6 An example of the sort of article you may read in the resources booklet. Use a highlighter and labels to pick out key points.

impacts of the floods

causes of flooding

opinions of local residents

Activities

1 **Discuss Figure 6.**
  a) Explain how floods can have social and economic impacts. Use evidence from the article.
  b) Identify reasons that may have led to flooding in Galgate. Sort these into two headings:
    Physical factors   *Human factors*
  c) Suggest two contrasting ways that residents in Galgate could have been better protected from this flood.
  d) Explain why it is impossible to protect every home from every flood.
2 **Imagine you are the AQA examiner. Suggest a question that could be asked about this resource that would require students to make a decision.**

Learning objectives

- How to structure your answer using argument and counter-argument.

Constructing an argument

The examiners may have identified an issue in the Pre-release resources booklet and plan to ask a question in the exam that starts *'To what extent'*. For example, based on the information in Figure 6, the cause of the flood is one issue. Another issue is what can be done to protect people from future floods. You should think carefully about the issues that occur in the resources and try setting yourself some 'To what extent' questions. Figure 7 gives you some ideas.

Figure 7 Use the resources booklet to practise 'To what extent' questions.

Identify any geographical issues that occur in the resources booklet. Create a strong statement about this issue. You could work in pairs to do this – or your teacher might do it for you.

'It is impossible to prevent every flood. People who live in areas affected by floods should do more to reduce the damage in their homes.'
To what extent do you agree?

'People are mainly to blame for flooding rather than natural processes.'
To what extent do you agree?

Argument. Use your knowledge and understanding of the issue, in this case floods and flood management, to construct an argument that supports your decision. You could use some of the phrases in Figure 8.

Counter-argument. It is very rare for a geographical issue to be straightforward. You should be able to think of reasons why some people would disagree with your decision. This is called a counter-argument. Use your knowledge and understanding of the issue to explore the counter-argument. See Figure 9 .

Conclusion. Make sure you show that you have considered 'to what extent' you think your argument outweighs the counter-argument. Figure 10 summarises the whole process of answering a question that asks you to make a decision.

First, decide 'to what extent' you agree. Then construct an argument using language that supports your decision. Use Figure 9 to help you.

Next, construct a counter-argument. Explain why some people might accept the opposite view to the one you have outlined in your argument. Use the sorts of phrases shown in Figure 8.

Where do
I fit?

0%   25%   50%   75%   100%

Completely disagree	Strongly disagree	Neutral	Strongly agree	Completely agree
There is clear evidence that …	Evidence suggests that …	Evidence is inconclusive	Evidence suggests that …	There is clear evidence that …
No impacts	Slight impacts	Some impacts	Significant impacts	Huge impacts
Of no importance	Little importance	Quite important	Very important	Extremely important
I can rule out	It is possible	I am undecided	I am confident	I am certain

Figure 8 Decide 'to what extent' you agree. Then construct an argument using language that supports your decision.

On the other hand … For example, some evidence suggests that …

Alternatively, it could be argued that … people would say this because …

My decision might have some negative impacts. For example, …

My decision might be opposed by some people. For example, …

Figure 9 Construct a counter-argument. Explain why some people might accept the opposite view to the one you have outlined in your argument. Use these sorts of phrases

1. State whether you agree or disagree

2. Use evidence to construct a supporting argument. Include the strongest evidence. If relevant, predict the positive outcomes of your decision, for example, positive impacts for people, the economy, or environment.

3. Consider opposite views to construct a counter-argument. If relevant, consider any negative outcomes of your decision.

4. Conclude your argument by restating whether you agree or disagree and give the main reason why.

On the one hand

On the other hand

Figure 10 How to construct an answer when you have been asked for a decision. The size of the block in the diagram suggests the length of this part of your answer.

Part 4 Preparing for Paper 3

113

Learning objectives

- What to revise for Section B – the assessment of your fieldwork;
- How to make revision active – doing things to help you learn rather than just reading your notes.

Figure 1 An example of how you will be asked your own experie fieldwork.

How to revise fieldwork

You should have kept notes about each of your fieldwork enquiries in a notebook or portfolio. When you revise these notes, the thing you need to remember is the title of each of your investigations. That's because the questions in the exam will ask you to identify the title of your investigation before you answer the question itself. Look at the example shown in Figure 1. In this example, all of the marks are for the evaluation itself. In fact, Section B only assesses AO3 analyse, evaluate, or make a judgement and AO4 use geographical skills (see pages 106-107) so, in your revision, you need to focus on things like:

- how well you can **evaluate** your fieldwork, or write a convincing argument;
- your ability to **use** the graph, map, and numeracy skills that are used during fieldwork investigations.

> This could be a hypothesis or enquiry question.

> You will be asked about each of your investigations.

State the title of your fieldwork enquiry in which **physical** geography data was collected.

Title of fieldwork enquiry: ....

....

Suggest one way in which your data collection methods could have been improved.

[3 marks]

> This is the command word.

> This means that you must think critically about your fieldwork when you revise. You don't need to describe data collection – you need to evaluate it.

Figure 2 Checklist to prepare for Paper 3, Section B.

Make a checklist

Use the checklist in Figure 2 to make sure you are prepared for Paper 3, Section B.

Task	I've done it
1 I have **organised** my fieldwork portfolio and I have notes about each of the fieldwork enquiries.	
2 I know the **title** for each of my fieldwork enquiries.	
3 I remember the **aims** of each enquiry.	
4 I understand the **sampling** methods we used and I can give at least one detailed reason why we used them.	
5 I can **evaluate** the strengths **and** weaknesses of the data collection methods we used to give a **balanced** answer.	
6 I can assess whether the maps and graphs that I drew were **suitable** and **effective** ways to represent my data.	
7 I can use **evidence** from my fieldwork to reach conclusions.	
8 I can discuss the **reliability** and **accuracy** of the data I used.	
9 I can give **three** ways that my fieldwork could be **improved**.	

Revising data collection

You could use the questions in Figure 3 to help evaluate the data collection phase of the enquiry.

How?	How many sample points did I use?	Was this the right number to use? Would trends have been clearer if I had used more?
Where?	Where did I collect my primary data? Where did I start and end the transect?	With hindsight, were these the best places? Was I able to use the data to draw a map?
Why?	Why did I choose the particular sampling strategy that was used?	Did I use systematic, random, stratified, or opportunistic sampling? Can I justify my choice?
What might?	What might have happened if I had used a different sampling strategy?	Could a different strategy have been better?
When?	When was the data collected?	Was time of day or time of the week an important factor? What might have happened if I had collected data at a different time?
Which?	Which pieces of equipment worked best? Which parts of the data collection sheets could have been improved?	Was the equipment working? Did everyone use it in the same way so that I got reliable results? To what extent was a pilot survey useful in helping me design the data collection sheets?

Revision objectives

My revision objectives are to evaluate how well I collected data for my enquiry.
- Could the data collection sheets have been improved?
- Can I justify the way data was sampled?
- What are the strengths and weaknesses of the data collection methods?

Figure 3 Questions to ask yourself about the data collection phase

Fish bone diagrams like Figure 4 are a useful way to analyse the factors involved in any process. Drawing a fish bone diagram should help you to evaluate each factor that may have affected your data collection. The first thing to do is to list all of the factors that might have had any effect on how data was collected – these become the bare bones of your diagram. Then, you can think about the strengths and weaknesses of each of these factors. It may help you to identify some simple ways that your data collection could have been improved.

Figure 4 Use a fish bone diagram to think about the strengths and weaknesses of each factor that contributed to the process of collecting the data.

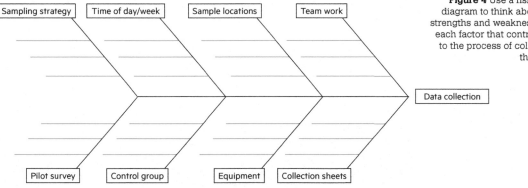

Sampling strategy   Time of day/week   Sample locations   Team work

Data collection

Pilot survey   Control group   Equipment   Collection sheets

Activities

1. Discuss the sampling strategy you used to collect your primary data. Make sure you understand why it was chosen and make some notes that **justify** this choice.
2. Study Figure 4.
   a) Make a large copy of this fish bone diagram. Keep the main heading of 'data collection' but think carefully about the factors – the headings at the end of each main bone. Most of them should be appropriate for your own fieldwork but, if some aren't, you should replace them.
   b) Think about the strengths and weaknesses of each factor. Add some notes to each minor 'bone' of the diagram.

Revising processing and presenting the data

Graphs and maps are ways of presenting your data in a visual form. They make it easier to see patterns or trends within your data. They also make it possible to compare data easily.

There are lots of different types of graph you can draw. But choosing which graph to draw is not just about personal taste. There are some rules about which graphs you can use. So, when you are revising, you need to think about:
- whether you chose the most suitable type of map or graph;
- the strengths and weaknesses of the maps and graphs in your portfolio;
- if you were going to draw one of them again, how you might do it better.

You can use a Lotus Diagram to think about how effective you were at processing and presenting your data. A Lotus Diagram is a simple way to break a big process (like data presentation of your fieldwork data) down into smaller chunks. To draw a Lotus Diagram use the following steps.

Step One Draw a grid of nine squares in the centre of a large sheet of paper.

Step Two Write the process that you want to evaluate in the middle square.

Step Three Now break that process down into eight smaller chunks and write those down in each of the eight outer squares. You could do this step in discussion with friends in class. Figure 5 shows an example.

Step Four Colour each of these eight squares in a different colour.

Step Five Draw another eight grids, each with nine squares. Write down each technique or factor from your first grid in the central cell of each new grid. An example of the complete grid with its 9 rows and 9 columns is shown in Figure 6.

Step Six Evaluate how well your fieldwork went in each of these areas. Again, you could do this as a discussion with friends in class. Remember to think about strengths and limitations of the techniques you used. Try to think of eight different statements. It isn't essential to fill every cell in the grid. An example is shown in Figure 7.

Figure 5 Eight aspects of processing and presentation arranged around the central part of a Lotus diagram.

Photographs	Transects and cross sections	Numeracy
Text	How was evidence processed and presented?	Maps and graphs
Perceptions	Making connections	Change over time

Figure 6 The complete Lotus Diagram.

If we had recorded where each respondent lives we could have mapped the results to see any spatial patterns	Lots of open questions in the questionnaire were time-consuming to process	I used word clouds to analyse responses to open questions which proved that some positive adjectives were used by many
Processing the pilot survey gave unexpected results and helped create a better questionnaire	Perceptions	I used a line graph to process the Likert survey scores. With hindsight, this was unsuitable because the data is not continuous
It was difficult to process the positive and negative numbers in the bipolar scores	Bipolar scores were represented with bar charts because this is discrete data	Mean bipolar scores were calculated for different age groups

Figure 7 An example of a completed Lotus Diagram which evaluates one aspect of data processing and presentation.

Chapter 15

Answering questions about fieldwork

Learning objectives

- Preparing for two different types of questions about fieldwork.

How fieldwork is assessed

Paper 3 Section B assesses your understanding of fieldwork. The questions could be about any of the six stages of the fieldwork enquiry process. There are two main types of question:

- questions about unfamiliar fieldwork. Parts 2 and 3 of this book contain examples of this type of question;
- questions about your own fieldwork. There are examples of this type of question on pages 121-125.

The questions in the exam will assess your ability to:

- analyse, or evaluate, or make a judgement (AO3) - 24 marks in total;
- use geographical skills (AO4) - 12 marks in total.

Questions about unfamiliar fieldwork

These questions will give you some information about how a student did their fieldwork. The information could be:

- a photograph of the fieldwork location;
- a table of data that has been collected;
- a map or graph to show how the student presented their data.

Some of these questions will be about physical geography fieldwork and others will be about human geography fieldwork. Study the information in the question paper carefully and then use it to answer the question that follows. For example, you could be asked to:

- use data to complete a graph or map, or to calculate a value such as a mean or interquartile range;
- use a photograph to suggest a potential fieldwork risk;
- identify a limitation in the way the student has collected data;
- evaluate the way that data has been presented.

Remember, these questions test your understanding of the process of fieldwork. Your own fieldwork may have been quite different to the example shown in the exam paper. But don't panic, you can still answer the question. Study Figure 1. Maybe your own physical fieldwork was in a river but the question shows a photo of fieldwork in a coastal location. You need to show that you can apply what you learned in your own fieldwork to this new situation.

Questions about your own fieldwork

Some questions will ask about your own fieldwork. These questions will test your ability to evaluate and make decisions. You will be asked to state the title of your

I identified the risks in my river fieldwork …

… but the question looks like this!

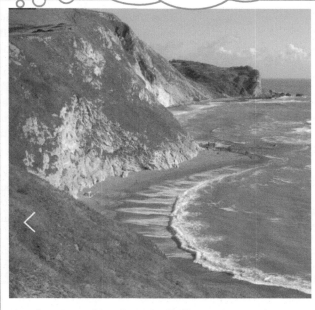

Identify two possible risks in this fieldwork location. [2]

The main risks in the river were (1) falling in the water and (2) river levels rising. I imagine there are similar risks here: (1) falling from the cliff and (2) the risk that the tide will rise, trapping people who are working on the beach.

Figure 1 Questions about unfamiliar fieldwork.

fieldwork (see page 114) but, apart from this, you don't need to describe your fieldwork. You need to show that you can:

- ▥ evaluate what you did;
- ▥ justify the decisions you made.

The examiner will want to see evidence that you can assess, evaluate, and make decisions – not simply describe what you did on the day of your field trip. For example:

- ▥ Can you explain why some ways of presenting your data might be more effective than other ways?
- ▥ Can you evaluate the strengths and weaknesses of your sampling techniques?

Exam advice

The questions are not about rivers or coasts. They are about the process of doing fieldwork. Prepare for the exam by thinking critically about how you did your own fieldwork. Then you can answer any question.

How to respond to command words

Exam advice
Spend about 10 minutes answering a 9 mark question.

Command words are words used at the beginning of a question such as Assess or Explain. The examiner will be checking that you do what the command word says. There are no marks for recall (remembering information) so there is no point spending any time simply **describing** what you did. Figure 2 lists the command words that could be used in Section B.

The other important information you need to think about is the tariff shown in square brackets at the end of the question. This is the maximum number of marks that can be awarded to the question. You should allow about one minute for every mark in this exam. So you should spend longer answering questions that are worth 6 or 9 marks than those worth 2 or 3 marks.

This is how to tackle a question:
■ read the question carefully;
■ identify the command word(s) – you could use a highlighter pen;
■ check the tariff and work out roughly how long to spend on the question;
■ pause part way through and make sure you are responding properly to the command word.

Figure 2 Command words that could be used in Section B.

Command words	What you need to do	Example practice question
Assess	Make an informed judgement. Weigh up the evidence for and against.	Assess how effective your presentation techniques were for displaying your data.
Calculate	Work out the value of something by doing some maths. You must show how you got your answer.	Calculate the interquartile range of the pebble sizes in Figure 1. Show your working.
Compare	Describe the similarities and differences between two things. Make sure that you do more than describe one thing and then the other. Use connectives such as 'similarly' or 'by contrast' so that you make direct comparisons.	Compare the distribution of pebble sizes in Figures 2 and 3.
Complete	Finish a task by adding information. In Section B you could be given some data and asked to complete a graph or map.	Complete the scatter graph using the data below.
Describe	Give a detailed account of something. In Section B you could be asked to describe a graph. If so, write about the trends or patterns that you can see.	Describe the trend shown on the line graph above.
Evaluate	Weigh up the positives and negatives, or strengths and limitations of something. Try to be balanced – so if you have described some strengths try to describe some limitations as well.	Evaluate the use of secondary data in your human geography enquiry.
Explain	Show your understanding by giving reasons. Always try to expand a simple statement by using connectives such as 'so', 'therefore', 'because', or 'consequently'.	Explain why the conclusions of your fieldwork may not be fully reliable.
Identify	Name or give a brief description of something.	Identify one potential risk in the fieldwork location shown in the photograph.
Justify	Show your understanding of a decision by giving your reasons for it. Make sure you give one or more detailed reasons. This is likely to be better than giving a list of simple statements.	Justify one technique you used to present data in your physical geography enquiry.
Suggest	Propose a possible solution, reason, or consequence.	Suggest one way that this graph could be improved.
To what extent	Make a judgement about the importance or success of some aspect of your fieldwork. Always support this judgement by giving one or more detailed reasons.	To what extent did your sample size affect the reliability of your results?

Answering questions about your own fieldwork

Study the example questions in Figure 3. Remember that, in the exam paper, questions about your own fieldwork will begin by asking you to state the title of your physical/human geography fieldwork enquiry. There are three key things that the examiner will be looking for in your answer.

1 Have you responded to the command word?

If the command is '**assess**' or '**evaluate**' use words such as *'On the one hand'*, *'the main strength of this technique'*, *'on the other hand'*, *'a major limitation'* to clearly signal that you are evaluating.

2 Have you written about an actual fieldwork experience?

Whether you collected data in a river, on a beach, or busy high street, make sure the examiner knows about it. The examiner wants to see evidence that you have been doing fieldwork, not just learning about it in the classroom.

3 Have you elaborated your answers?

Extended answers that use connectives like *'so'*, *'therefore'*, *'because'* are usually much better than responses that use short, simple statements.

Exam advice

Don't be tempted to write everything you know about your fieldwork. Look at the command word carefully and make sure you answer it.

Stage of the enquiry process	Example question about fieldwork	Tariff
Creating aims and selecting suitable questions	1. Identify one strength and one limitation of the aim of your human geography fieldwork enquiry.	2 marks
	2. Assess the suitability of the location used for your fieldwork enquiry.	6 marks
Selecting, measuring and recording data	3. Compare the reliability of two ways of collecting primary data in your physical geography fieldwork enquiry.	6 marks
	4. Evaluate the sampling strategies you used in your own fieldwork enquiry.	6 marks
Processing and presenting fieldwork data	5. Justify one presentation technique you used to present primary data from your fieldwork.	3 marks
	6. Assess the effectiveness of the techniques you used to present your data.	6 marks
Analysing fieldwork data	7. Justify one technique you used to analyse your results.	3 marks
	8. Suggest reasons for any anomalies in your fieldwork data.	6 marks
Reaching conclusions	9. To what extent did your conclusions meet the aims or predictions of your fieldwork?	9 marks
	10. To what extent did the evidence you collected allow you to reach reliable conclusions?	9 marks
Evaluating the enquiry	11. Evaluate the reliability of the secondary data you used in your fieldwork enquiry.	6 marks
	12. To what extent was your fieldwork enquiry limited by problems with data collection methods?	9 marks

Figure 3 Example questions about your own fieldwork.

Activities

1 Study each of the questions in Figure 3.
   a) Working in pairs, copy out one question and highlight the key words.
   b) Discuss how you are going to answer the question.
   c) Answer the question independently, making sure you use the right amount of time.
   d) Peer review each other's work. Try to identify two positive things about your friend's work and one thing that could be improved.

Sample answers

Read each of the sample answers that follow. Read the answer **before** you read the examiner comment. Things to think about:

1. Has the candidate responded clearly to the **command word** – or is the answer just a description of fieldwork?

2. Has the candidate used **evidence** from their actual fieldwork?

3. Have they fully **elaborated** their answer – or could they add something to make the meaning even clearer?

Responses about selecting, measuring, and recording data

3 **Compare the reliability of two ways of collecting qualitative data.** **[6 marks]**

Student response 1

I used bipolar surveys and photography to collect qualitative data about how Birmingham city centre is changing. I found some old photos online and then photographed the same place as it is today. I found both of these techniques provided useful data but the re-photography was the better technique because it was more reliable. The bipolar surveys gave me useful information about how people feel about change which is something re-photography cannot do. However, I don't think that bipolar surveys are very reliable because I think responses from members of the public might vary depending on whether they were in a hurry or not whereas re-photography doesn't suffer from this kind of issue. The main limitation with re-photography is that I couldn't find old photos of all of the places I wanted to survey. I could find old pictures of main streets but not of less well known places. However, a strength of this technique is that it was really easy to find exactly the right place to take my own photos.

Examiner's comment

Student response 1 is excellent. The first sentence is recall but it is short so time hasn't been wasted. It will help the examiner understand the rest of the answer. The student makes several direct comparisons between the use of bipolar surveys and photography which shows that they are responding to the command word. The response is balanced because the student refers to strengths and weaknesses of each technique.

Student response 2

I used bipolar surveys and I took photographs which I annotated. It was easy to take lots of photos but it was raining when I took some of them so they aren't as clear as I would like. I didn't really enjoy doing the bipolar surveys very much because people didn't really want to spend much time talking to me. We used random sampling because that is the least biased type of sampling.

Examiner's comment

Student response 2 shows limited ability to evaluate. It's not a good idea to write about what you like or dislike as this isn't really an evaluation of the fieldwork. It's not very balanced because the answer doesn't really talk about strengths. No direct comparisons are made. The final sentence may be true but the student doesn't explain why random is unbiased or make the statement in connection with their actual fieldwork.

4 Evaluate the sampling techniques you used in your own fieldwork enquiry. **[6 marks]**

Student response 1

We used systematic sampling to investigate pedestrian flows. We selected 16 sample points that were 80 metres apart. The advantage of systematic sampling is it ensured a wide coverage of the CBD so we could collect plenty of data and look for spatial patterns. This meant that our sample area included some places with lots of chain stores in the centre of the CBD and other places on the edge of the CBD where it was mainly independent shops so we could compare these different places. Other sampling strategies such as opportunistic and random may not have allowed this comparison.

One weakness of our sampling method was that there were so many sites it was difficult to survey them all in one day and they covered a large area. So we were very rushed and some data may have been inaccurate.

> The student has written an answer which has structure. It is obvious that this is an evaluation because of the use of words like 'advantage' and weakness'.

> One advantage of systematic sampling is that it captures the way data changes along a line or over space. This response is excellent because it explains that advantage by referring to the context of shops in different parts of the city. An answer that could be about sampling any data anywhere would not be as good.

Student response 2

When we collected our data for the size of the pebbles downstream we used the sampling technique of random. We did this 5 times for each area of the river. 5 times left, middle and right. This worked well as in our graphs it clearly shows what was meant to happen because as we went along the river the size got smaller and shape got rounder.

We had some issues with human error and accuracy when taking the time for the plastic ball to travel down the river the person taking the time could have stopped the clock too early or too late. Accessibility was another thing because some sites weren't accessible to us.

> This first part of this paragraph is description rather than an evaluation. The highlighted sentence implies an advantage but no reasons are given for why the sampling 'worked well'.

> 'We had some issues' is a bit vague for evaluation. It's better to be really clear, for example, 'One weakness of this sampling'.

> This final sentence needs elaborating. Why weren't they accessible and how did this affect the quality of sampling?

Responses about the reliability of data

11 Evaluate the reliability of secondary data you used in your fieldwork enquiry. **[6 marks]**

Student response 1

The advantage of using satellite images is that they show the whole area and a detailed image of an area. They are often updated, unlike other maps. On the other hand, they don't show everything. For example, in the middle course of the River Onny it is covered in shrubs and trees so we couldn't find secondary data from the image for all of our sites.

> Yellow highlighted words clearly signal that this is evaluation.

> Green highlighted phrases are the advantages/disadvantages. The first two are true but apply to lots of data. The last one is the more successful because it is about the actual fieldwork.

Student response 2

I used crime data from Police UK. This secondary data allowed me to see if the number of pedestrians in different parts of the city centre was influenced by crime. Furthermore, this data comes from a reliable source. Police UK is an unbiased organisation that wouldn't give fake data. However, there are disadvantages. Secondary crime data was taken from a large area which means that it does not give clear, accurate and precise information on crime for the small neighbourhoods of the city that I visited.

> Yellow highlighted words are a bit vague – how could this be made more evaluative?

> The green highlighted part of this response is excellent. A general disadvantage is that secondary data is often collected over a much larger area than your primary data. This response explains that disadvantage using specific detail from their own fieldwork

Activities

1 **Choose one of these responses. Identify:**
   a) Two things that work well.
   b) One thing that could be improved.

Glossary

2D Two dimensional. A line such as a cross section or transect.

Accuracy How close a measurement is to the true value of the object that is being measured.

Aim What you hope to achieve or prove through fieldwork.

Altitude The height above sea level.

Analysis A process in which you make sense of the evidence.

Anemometer A piece of fieldwork equipment used to measure wind speed.

Annotation Text added to a photo or artwork to analyse and highlight key features of the image.

Anomaly Data that does not fit into the general pattern or trend.

AONB Area of Outstanding Natural Beauty. Countryside in the UK that is protected and conserved.

Assess To use data and evidence to make a judgement.

Average The central point of a data set. The average can be expressed in three ways:
Mean Calculated by adding up all the data in a set of data to find the total and then dividing that total by the number of items of data.
Median The middle value when all the data in a set of data in arranged in rank order.
Mode The most frequently occurring value in a set of data.

Axis/y/x The x-axis is the horizontal base line of a graph. The y-axis is the vertical line.

Backwash The flow of water down a beach after a wave has broken.

Bar chart A way to represent data. Values are shown using vertical columns or horizontal bars.
Divided bar A rectangle which has been divided into segments to represent data in the form of percentages.

Beach profile A cross section showing the landscape of a beach, both above the water and below it.

Belt transect (continuous & interrupted) A sampling strategy. Data is collected along a line (or transect) usually by using a quadrat.

Bias A tendency to be positive or negative about something or someone.

Big data Large sets of data and databases of secondary data such as the National Census.

Bipolar survey A data collection method in which people express an opinion by choosing from opposite pairs of statements.

Brownfield site An area of land that has been used for one type of use or commercial activity that can be redeveloped for a different purpose such as retail, offices, or housing.

Callipers An instrument for measuring the distance between two opposite sides of an object such as a pebble.

Breaks in slope Places along a transect where the gradient of the slope suddenly changes.

Causality The relationship between something that happens or exists and the thing that makes it happen.

CBD Central Business District – the town or city centre.

Central tendency The central point or average of a dataset.

Chain stores National networks of stores under the same ownership.

Choropleth A type of map where darker colours (or darker shading) are used to represent higher data values

Climate change A large-scale, long-term change in the Earth's weather patterns or average temperatures.

Clinometer A piece of fieldwork equipment used to measure gradient / slope angle.

Clone town A geographical concept. How towns/cities have lost their local identity because most of the locally owned shops and businesses have been replaced by national chain stores.

Closed questions Questions with specific set answers so that the person answering has to choose the answer that they most agree with.

Cluster(ed) A group of similar things gathered or occurring closely together.

Command word Word used at the beginning of a question such as Assess or Explain.

Commuting The movement of people between their home and work place.

Concept A big idea that helps us make sense of geography.

Conceptual framework A geographical concept (or big idea) that gives your fieldwork a purpose.

Conclusion A summary statement or judgement that summarises the findings of a fieldwork enquiry.

Conflict matrix A way to record potential conflicts, for example between different uses of a place or space.

Connection The link that exists between one set of data and another.

Control group A group of data that acts as a benchmark. A researcher can compare the results from the sampled group to the control group to help identify the impact of different variables.

Control readings Measurements that are taken so that the effects of one variable can be isolated from an investigation.

Correlation The connection that links two sets of data (or variables) together.
Negative correlation Values in one set of data increase as values in the other set of data decrease.
Positive correlation Values in both sets of data increase at the same time.

Counting To record how many whole units there are.

Cross section Represents the shape or profile of a feature using measurements of the distances and depths from a horizontal line.

Cycles A geographical concept. How some processes are connected to one another through a system of flows and cycles. The water cycle is a good example.

Data Facts and statistics collected together, for example, as evidence and for analysis.
Big data A very large and complex set of data.
Bivariate data Two sets of data that are connected in some way.
Census data Data about the whole population which is collected every 10 years.
Continuous data Values that can be measured and recorded to one or more decimal point.
Discrete data Values that can be counted and recorded as whole numbers.
Primary data Data that is collected first hand.
Qualitative data Evidence that is collected as words, opinions, or images.
Quantitative data Evidence that is collected as number values.
Secondary data Data that has already been published in another source.

Dataset A group of values (set of data) that is often presented in a table.

Deindustrialisation The decline in industrial activity in a town or region.

Deprivation A lack of the things (such as work, money, good health or education) that are needed for a reasonable quality of life in modern society.

Desire line map Uses thin straight lines to show how places are linked together.

Dispersion graph A way to represent data. Data is plotted to show the range of values.

Diversification A process which makes the economy more varied. For example, the economy of the countryside used to depend mainly on farming but the introduction of a range of leisure or tourism jobs has diversified the rural economy.

Dot map Uses individual dots to show the exact location of similar features on a map.

Egan's Wheel A way of presenting the characteristics of sustainable communities named after Sir John Egan.

Elaborate To write an extended answer that links ideas and often uses connectives like 'so', 'therefore', 'because'.

Elaboration To create longer sentences that show you fully understand something, often using connective words like 'so', 'because', 'therefore', 'which means that' to link ideas together.

Enquiry process The process by which a student collects and analyses evidence in order to make a decision or prove/disprove an aim.

Engineering

Hard - Coastal management strategies such as building sea walls, groynes, or the use of rock armour (large boulders).

Soft – Coastal management through more natural methods such as re-profiling and beach nourishment (adding sand or shingle) and management of sand dunes.

Environment The surroundings or conditions in which a person, animal, or plant exists.

EQI (Environmental Quality Index) A technique which uses detailed criteria (statements) to assess the quality of our surroundings.

Erosion A process by which the land is worn away.

Evaluate To weigh up the strengths (or advantages) against the weaknesses (or disadvantages).

Evaluation A process in which you weigh up strengths and limitations. Evaluation is an important stage in your fieldwork enquiry in which you assess how well your fieldwork has gone. For example, you can evaluate the methods you used to collect or represent data.

Evidence Information that can be used to investigate an aim, test a hypothesis, or support an argument. Evidence may include quantitative or qualitative data.

Extrapolation A process by which a graph is used to find a data value that lies outside (or beyond) other data values.

Feature A natural or built part of the environment.

Field sketch A sketch made during the fieldtrip which records evidence about the most important features of a fieldwork location.

Fieldwork Practical work undertaken in natural and urban environments to investigate geographical questions and hypotheses.

Flow line map A way to represent data. The amount of a flow (such as traffic or pedestrians) is shown using a proportional arrow.

Flow meter A piece of equipment to measure the velocity of the flow of a river.

Flows Movement of things through an environment, for example, water, people, money.

Food miles Measure of the distance your weekly shopping has travelled before it arrives on your plate.

Footfall A measurement of the number of pedestrians.

Frequency The rate at which something happens over a particular period of time.

Geological map A way to represent data. Rock types are shown on a map by using different colours.

Geographical concepts Big ideas that help us understand how the world works.

Gentrification The process of improvement of run down or dilapidated buildings and areas through attraction of more affluent sectors of society.

GIS Geographic Information System A system which captures, stores, analyses, and presents types of geographical data.

Google street view A feature in Google Maps and Google Earth that provides panoramic views from positions along many streets in the world.

Grid reference A reference which describes a location on a map via a series of vertical and horizontal grid lines identified by numbers and letters.

Histogram A type of graph that uses bars to represent continuous data.

Honeypot site A place that attracts many visitors, like bees around a honeypot.

Hypothesis A statement which can be proven to be correct or incorrect based on the evidence collected in your fieldwork.

Identity A geographical concept. The features that make a place special or unique.

Inequality A geographical concept. The ways in which different groups of people have uneven access to such things as jobs, wealth, housing, or services.

Infiltration (rates) The speed at which rain water soaks into the soil.

Integrated transport Where different types of transport work together, for example, pedestrian, cycling routes linked to bus routes and train stations.

Interpolate/interpolation A process by which a graph is used to find a data value that lies between other data values.

Interquartile range The middle 50% of a data set. The range from Q1-Q3.

Interview A way of collecting qualitative data. Interviews involve asking open questions. An interview is usually less structured and may be more detailed than a questionnaire.

Investigation Using enquiry skills to test a hypothesis or answer a question by collecting and analysing data and evidence.

Irregular Not regular. Does not fit a pattern or set of rules.

Isoline map A way to represent data. Data points with the same value are joined by a line.

Judgement A decision that you must support by use of evidence.

Key The legend of a map or graph that describes the meaning of colours or symbols that have been used.

Landform A natural feature in the landscape.

Line graph A way to represent data. Values are shown by drawing a line that joins the data together.

Linear Arranged along a straight or nearly straight line.

Likert survey A data collection method in which people express an opinion by stating how strongly they agree or disagree with statements.

Logarithmic A scale on a graph where the numbers increase more and more rapidly.

Mean A measure of central tendency (or average) in a dataset.

Meanders Sweeping bends that develop as a landform on many rivers.

Measuring/measurement The action of calculating the size, length, distance, area, quantity, depth, range of something.

Median A measure of central tendency (or average) in a dataset.

Mode/modal class A measure of central tendency (or average) in a dataset.

Multinational companies Operating in more than one country, usually several.

NEE This stands for Newly Emerging Economy. It means a country that is undergoing rapid economic growth.

NIMBY This stands for Not In My Back Yard. It means that people don't want a particular development (like a new runway) built close to where they live.

Open questions These allow the person being interviewed to say whatever they want in response.

Opportunistic A sampling strategy. Data is sampled where it is convenient to do so.

Ordnance Survey (OS) maps Online and paper maps that show the landscape features of the UK.

Origin The place on a graph where the two axes meet.

Pattern A regular form or sequence that can be seen.

Perception What someone thinks of a place, idea, situation.

Physical process A series of natural actions that change a feature over time.

Pictogram A way to represent data. A simple picture is used to show the value of data.

Pie chart A type of graph where a circle is divided into segments that each represent a proportion of the whole.

Pilot survey A stage of data collection that allows sampling methods to be tried out and evaluated before a full sample is taken.

Place A geographical concept. The features that give each location a sense that it is different from other locations.

Pocket park Small green spaces in urban areas that benefit the local community and the environment.

Point bar A beach on the inside bend of a meander formed by the deposition of sediment (also known as a slip off slope).

Pre-release resources booklet Provided to students 12 weeks prior to the Paper 3 exam. It provides information on a geographical issue which will be examined in Section A of the exam.

Profile An outline that represents a feature as seen from one side.

Beach profile A diagram that represents the gradients of a beach.

Long Profile A diagram that describes how a feature such as a river varies along its length.

Proportional symbol map Uses symbols (usually squares or circles) of different sizes to represent data.

Quadrat A piece of fieldwork equipment. A square frame that is used to sample data (often vegetation).

Quality of life The standard of health, comfort, and happiness experienced by an individual or group.

Questionnaire A way of collecting qualitative data that involves asking a number of respondents a common set of questions.

Random number table A table of digits (0 to 9) arranged in an unpredictable sequence in rows and columns and used to create a random sample.

Range Measure of dispersion – the difference between the highest and lowest value in a dataset.

Rank order A process by which numbers are put into sequence by their value from largest to smallest.

Reliability The degree to which the evidence collected during an investigation can be considered consistent and dependable.

Re-photography The process of taking a photograph now (primary data) and comparing it to a photograph or other image taken in the past (secondary data).

Representative Sampled data that is a true reflection of the whole.

Resources Booklet – see Pre-release resources booklet.

Risk A geographical concept. A possibility or threat of damage, injury, danger.

River discharge Amount of water flowing per second down a river channel.

Rural diversification A wider range of jobs and commercial activity beyond traditional activities such as farming.

Rural environment An area of countryside including farms, villages, and smaller towns.

Sample A small part or quantity that can show what the whole of something is like, for example, a group of people drawn from the population of an area used to show what that population is like.

Sampling The process of selecting a sample.

Random Data is sampled at irregular intervals.

Regular Data is sampled at equal intervals.

Stratified Data is sampled in proportion to the size of the original population.

Systematic Data is sampled at regular intervals.

Transect Data is sampled along a line.

Scale line A visual way of showing distance on a map by drawing a short line to a known length.

Scatter graph A way to represent bivariate data. Data points for two variables are shown on the same graph.

Settlement A place where people live.

Sketch A simple drawing that represents the main features of a landscape.

Sketch map A simple plan that represents the main features of a landscape.

Slip off slope A beach on the inside bend of a meander formed by the deposition of sediment (also known as a point bar).

SMART A statement, aim, or objective which is Specific, Measurable, Achievable, Realistic, and Timely.

Socio-economic A way of classifying people. The 'socio' part describes their social position (for example, by education). The 'economic' part describes their income (for example, by their occupation).

Spatial pattern How features are distributed across a map.

Species A group of living things with similar characteristics.

Sphere of influence A geographical concept. The area around a geographical feature affected by it.

Store(s) A geographical concept. An accumulation or stock of something, for example, an ocean is a store of water.

Suburb The outer zone of a town or city.

Sustainability A geographical concept. A measure of how well a place or an environment is coping with social, economic, or environmental change.

Swash The movement of water up a beach each time a wave breaks.

Tariff In an exam, the maximum number of marks that can be awarded to the question.

Tally mark A quick way to keep track of numbers. A vertical line equals one. Tally marks are made in groups of five. One vertical line for each of the first four numbers and a diagonal line for the fifth.

Text analysis Looking for patterns or trends in words.

Trampling To tread on or crush, for example, plants in the environment.

Transect An imaginary line through the environment. Data and observations can be made along this line.

Trend A change shown on a graph.

Urban environment A human settlement such as a town, city, or area that is made up of buildings, roads and other built features.

Urban regeneration Redevelopment of towns and cities; old buildings are replaced by new buildings and sites developed for new uses.

Variable A feature, element, or factor which changes.

Dependant variable A variable whose value depends on the value of another factor (such as distance, time, or height).

Independent variable A factor that causes other data to vary.

Vegetation Plants, shrubs, trees.

Velocity The speed at which something flows.

Index